By the Editor:

She and I: A Fugue

Human Days: A Mary MacLane Reader

I Await the Devil's Coming: Annotated & Unexpurgated

Tender Darkness: A Mary MacLane Sampler

http://fuguewriter.com

*

Coming soon:

Mary in The Press:
Miss MacLane and Her Fame

A Quite Unusual Intensity of Life:
The Lives, Works and Influence of
Mary MacLane

(with Chiara di Benedetto)

MOCKING MARY

The Humorists vs. Miss MacLane

EDITED, WITH AN INTRODUCTION &
NOTES, BY MICHAEL R. BROWN

PETRARCA PRESS
AUSTIN · TEXAS
2015

First edition.

Printed in the USA.

This paper is PH-balanced.
It should undergo lessened crumbling, yellowing,
or other deterioration over time.

BIBLIOGRAPHIC DATA

Brown, Michael R., ed., 1965-
Mocking Mary: the humorists vs. Miss MacLane
1st ed. / p. cm.
Lib. of Congress Control No. PENDING
1. Feminism - United States - Literary collections
2. Women - United States - Literary collections
ISBN 978-1-883304-06-5 - Paperbound
ISBN 978-1-883304-10-2 - Casebound

Table of Contents

Introduction

THE REDISCOVERY of Mary MacLane's first book - which received an Australian stage homage in 2012, a widely-discussed US edition of March 2013, a Danish translation later that year, a Spanish edition in January 2015 - has made the once-inescapable tale of its success again familiar: shortly after book publication of her proto-blog *I Await the Devil's Coming* (under the publisher's colorless title *The Story of Mary MacLane*) in April 1902, a spectacular success flowed up to the twenty-one year old author and the several literary genres she'd opened.

Mostly lost to history, in the foam and surges and following undertows, has been the coincident silly season: the cross-country binge of humor, in every possible genre, centering on the young prodigy. Bits have been discussed in recent years - for the most part in obscure venues, as in unpublished doctoral dissertations - but its full extent, as with the rest of the immense press and literary reaction to MacLane, remains unexplored.

We do know that before 1902 was out a number of characters redolent of the young author had trodden New York stages: from a fresh-air Montana maiden on a mid-ocean passenger ship, to the outright parody named Mary McPain who matched wits with the Devil for seven months at one of the city's biggest vaudeville halls.

We know also that by year's end thousands of village and county and urban newspapers had poked fun. Among a daily paper's half-page of one or two-sentence items newsy or humorous or astonishing (to today's eyes curiously like a Tweet-flock) was sure to be a reference or two, direct or otherwise: intense young women, the Devil, Butte (and Montana), crushes on schoolmistresses, red sunsets, olives, toothbrushes - all facilely permutated and frothed together with other popular things. And there were thousands of items in the yellow press (some of them interviews, generally reprinted or invented) dovetailing with and reinforcing the ever-coming humor-jabs.

There were advantages, to be sure. It kept the author out in front and books selling - indeed, sold-out even in Boston that autumn. MacLane was put in involuntary symbiosis with the yellow press. Though it benefited in the near-term, her long-term prospects assumed a lemony dimness. It became possible to write her off as a mere attention-seeker. She'd never been respectable, never tried to be - but after the yellowing, she was tagged and thus made dismissable.

Some understood, and fought it. A professor at the University of Chicago, Oscar L. Triggs, declared that readers of MacLane's first book "will see the soul of a woman laid bare. Few people will probably have the strength and courage to read it, or the wit to understand." The great radical lawyer Clarence Darrow called it "little short of a miracle. No more marvelous book was ever born of a sensitive, precocious brain." The future magister of Berkeley's Bancroft Library (and Jack London's friend), Porter Garnett, declared MacLane of greater moment than Alfred Austin, Poet Laureate of England: "the one is sui generis, the other a mere variant."

But such voices - and there were not only three - were unheard over the yellow yells. She was a sensation, had been so marketed by her publishers (despite her having wanted to "avoid anything like mere cheap notoriety and sensationalism"), and there was no escape.

For all potential lost - of, say, more serious news covering, more probing interviews, more opportunities for her to gain an audience appreciative of her stylistic and spiritual power - we, a century later, find in the vari-colored splashes of the time an odd historical benefit then invisible: the pokes and jabs and giggles, all unguarded, show us not only how she was taken but what in its own right was found funny, mockable, loveable, dismissable. The lines thrown off by writers scrambling for a few cents, without time to think, provide an odd direct line to the inner rules of the world Mary MacLane challenged.

A forthcoming book from Petrarca Press - *Mary in The Press: Miss Mac-Lane and Her Fame* - will provide, in two volumes totaling over a thousand pages, a deep-going look into the literary industry that sprang up about her. Not included there, however - for reasons of space alone - are several extraordinary examples of media fever: no fewer than three books - two of 1902, one of 1903 - to focus, in intriguingly differing ways, on the young author.

These books - *The Story of Willie Complain*, *The Story of Lizzie McGuire*, and *The Devil's Letters to Mary MacLane* - are the present volume's core; it is their first republication and is the first study of their authors, ever.

Below will appear what is known of the three authors. *Willie* and *Lizzie* are straightforward parodies; each stands on its own. If one knows MacLane one sees the humor, and if not then one's been practicing literary asceticism. Read her, then resume here. *Letters* is a more complex case and occasions some analysis; about its author, almost nothing is known.

After the three, the editor offers up some noteworthy (*i.e.*, amusing or telling) pieces of humor from the press avalanche throughout the time of MacLane's fame. None has been previously reprinted.

*

Robert James Shores (1881-1950), author of *Willie*, seems to have been one of those wandering stones that gathered no moss and worried not about leaving a trace. One wouldn't have heard of him hadn't one looked, and it seems he'd have been just fine with that. From the traces left - and it's hazardous, inferring how people felt life from documentation-scraps - he seems to have been about enjoying his earth-time.

He was born in 1881 - within a month and 400-odd miles of MacLane - in Minneapolis, Minnesota to a long-lived family with Southern roots. Nothing's yet known of his childhood beyond a family move to Great Falls, Montana in the 1890s: the same move MacLane's family had made - also from Minnesota - nearly ten years earlier upon her widowed mother's remarriage. By 1898 Shores was editor-in-chief of the school newspaper (*cf. Anaconda Standard* [Montana], 10 Oct 1898, p 9), and the next year, freshly-graduated, was running a youth periodical called *The Patriot* - which, it was reported, would close when he left for college (*ibid.*, 24 April 1899, p 11 *&* 2 Dec 1899, p 11).

His sister Minnie married in Montana's Silver Bow County in 1902 - the same locale and year in which MacLane's sister would marry, in which Shores' book would be published, and in which his father - Arthur J. Shores, a lawyer in general practice - had become well-known. That year young Shores would graduate from Cornell in New York, return to Butte, and develop his writing - in part by publishing *Willie* under the imprint of MacLane's alternate champion and skewerer: Butte's *Inter Mountain* newspaper. Though he'd published a six-page collection of poems - *Ye Monster and Other Poems* - in 1899, *Willie* was his first book.

A year later, upon leaving Butte for a Seattle opportunity, he was feted for the excellence of his writing (*ibid.*, 29 Aug 1903, p 12); once relocated, he and journalist Ernestine Cochran (newly from Hawaii, who in Butte had as "Nan Byxbee" written of MacLane) would begin a humorous society weekly, the *Chit-Chat*. Shores' light, breezy style, a reporter averred, would be "a certain cure for the blues" (*Seattle Star*, 7 Nov 1903, p 5).

By 1904 he had begun publishing poetry in newspapers (*ibid.*, 1 Dec 1904, p 4) and magazines, which, together with newspaper writing, carried him to 1909 in New Jersey, residing with his parents, their butler, and a cook in the same year MacLane was living in the big city across the Hudson.

About that year he'd begun *The Idler* - a playful collection of "Ideas for Idle People," still extant two years later to be judged by a Montana paper "a delightful little monthly magazine, 'perpetrated and published by Robert J.

Shores'. 'Bobby' Shores has many friends in Montana: they will recognize the author in the pages of the magazine and they will see that he has not changed much since he lived in this state; the few years have brought maturer thought than our friend used to record when he wrote out here but there is the same sparkle and originality in his copy that used to be there" (*Daily Missoulian* [Montana], 27 Jan 1911, p 4). It lasted at least into 1913.

In 1909 Shores self-published a curious poetry volume of a few dozen pages - *At Molokai and Other Verse*, featuring an eponymous poem on Hawaii's Kalaupapa leper colony - and in 1910 was out with forty more poetry-pages, an odd mixture of Hellenism and amorousness titled *Gay Gods and Merry Mortals: Some Excursions in Verse*, issued by New York's established, high-volume, but often-potboiling Broadway Pub. Co. That year he authored a suggestive poem, "A Jest," subsequently anthologized (in, *e.g.*, T.R. Smith, ed., *Poetica Erotica: Rare and Curious Amatory Verse* [3 vols.], New York: Boni & Liveright, 1921-1922; apparent first pub. in *Current Opinion*, Feb 1910, pp 220-221).

He secured a mainstream publisher - Bobbs-Merrill - for a 1913 humor collection: *New Brooms*, a set of topical-subject letters supposedly received by *The Idler's* editor; it received its share of friendly notices (a number are quoted in *The Dial*, 16 Dec 1913, p 509 [advert.]).

A move to New York is apparent around the time of his marriage in 1914, and in any case he'd set up there as a publisher by 1915. In 1916 he was issuing novels and poetry-books - all by others - and by 1918 was soliciting mystery stories. He would have no further recorded activity as a publisher.

Shores had caught Elbert Hubbard's eye with a line that'd had newspaper currency - "Our hope for eternal life in the hereafter does not spring from a longing for a spiritual existence, but grows out of our love for life upon this earth, which we have tried and found good" - which won inclusion in *Elbert Hubbard's Scrap Book: Containing the Inspired and Inspiring Selections, Gathered During a Life Time of Discriminating Reading for His Own Use* (W.H Wise & Co, New York, 1923); apparent first pub. in Hubbard's *The Fra: For Philistines and Roycrofters*, Dec 1912, p iv; earliest known newspaper pub. *Logan Republican* [Utah], 21 Jan 1913, p 4.

This may have pointed the way for Shores' future. By 1929 he appears in a Washington D.C. city directory as the Rev. Shores of Saint Mary's Episcopal Church, and so he would remain: the 1930 census shows him as "Clergyman" and the 1940 as "Preacher."

His congregation, one trusts, walked out with lightened spirits. He didn't seem to lose an attraction to fun, for in 1932 the Rev. Shores and his wife copyrighted a fast fox-trot titled *Waddle I Do*.

He died, in 1950, in Washington, D.C.

*

Our next author, Frank Corey Voorhies (1887-1927), seemed to dwell under no such charmed sky. Or perhaps he had much happiness in his breast and cared yet less what happened outside of it, and strove with ambition but not much attention to make his way.

Born in 1877 to a very old Dutch New Jersey family - as "Van Voorheys" they hailed from the mid-17th century, though his father was a farmer and road-worker - he entered the Ivy League by way of Princeton University, where (after joining the Whist Club in 1897) he served as managing editor of 1898-1899 for their yearbook, the *Bric-a-Brac*.

By 1899 he'd gone into humor-writing, possibly college-tinctured, with a brief publication - *Dee Tees* (which Princeton, alone among libraries, honored with a shelving).

After graduation he became an assistant magazine editor and by 1901 broke into print with *The Love Letters of an Irishwoman* (Mutual Book Co., Boston) - a parody of that year's internationally successful, purportedly genuine *Love Letters of an Englishwoman*.

Having published his MacLane parody (Henry A. Dickerman *& Sons*, Boston, 1902), he hit a productive stretch in 1903 with several books: *Reflections of Bridget McNulty* (Dickerman Pub. Co., Boston), which contained assorted musings of an Irish serving-girl on varying topics, styled in heavy brogue; *The Knocker* (Mutual Book Co., Boston, which had bought Dickerman *& Sons*), a take-off on human types: floorwalkers, sour-pusses, publishers, etc.; and *Mrs. McPiggs' [sic.] of the Very Old Scratch: A Half Grown Novel* (Mutual Book Co., Boston), a parody of the extremely popular 1901 novel *Mrs. Wiggs of the Cabbage Patch*.

The next year would see his humorous account of the USA from Columbus to the Revolution in *Twisted History* (G.W. Dillingham, New York; advert. in *The Sun* [New York], 23 Mar 1904, p 9).

After this he published nothing under his own name but found success somewhere, for in 1907 we find him and his wife among the elect in a magnificent Cambridge apartment house - Riverbank Court, on the Charles River esplanade - and so listed in that year's *Blue Book of Cambridge* and *Clark's Boston Blue Book*. (In the latter's 1901 edition he'd appeared resident at The Westminster in Copley Square.)

1909 brings a surprise, then, with a cross-country flood of classified ads under his name that would appear for several years (and in *Popular Science* from 1909-1910), seeking men to work from home to earn $383/month in 1909 (*Evening Star* [Washington, D.C.], 21 Feb 1909, pt 7, p 8) and $200/ week in 1910 (*Salt Lake Herald-Republican* [Utah], 6 Nov 1910, Real Estate/ Classified, p 1).

The 1910 census shows him as operator of a mail order business out of Omaha, Nebraska. On 19 Mar 1911 a final ad - promising "money comes in every day" - appears (*Washington Times* [Washington, D.C.], 19 Mar 1911, p 18), and then there are no more.

In 1915 he informs fellow alumni that he's in the fire extinguisher business, still in Omaha, and possessor of a fine house and big car (*Princeton Alumni Weekly*, 17 Nov 1915, p 184).

By 1918, he is managing the Duchess Drug Manuf. Co. in Minneapolis, and by 1920 he authors - under the pseudonym "John Martin" - a booklet on running a mail order business successfully while reporting on that year's census that he continued to manage a drug manufacturing company in Minneapolis.

That same year, *Office Appliances* ("The Magazine of Office Equipment") reported: "The Mutual Manufacturing Company will manufacture ink and office supplies. Capital stock, $410,000; incorporators, F.C. Voorhees, L.M. Voorhees and Annie Fluor, Minneapolis, Minn." (May 1920, p 208).

There seems to be nothing further until his death.

Let us hope that his way, restless to outward record, was filled with happiness.

He died in April 1927 in Marblehead Neck, Massachusetts. His books and history have attracted no attention until now.

*

None of the three books had any detectable influence on the others, and each exists in the timeless moment of humor. The last-written is therefore first in this collection - the longest, most substantial, and best introduction to the culture out of which they came: *The Devil's Letters to Mary MacLane*.

To dispose of a persistent bibliographic error: pleasing as a fourth book from her would be, MacLane didn't write it. Though published anonymously ("By Himself"), the publisher submitted author information to the Library of Congress: uniquely among the parodies, and rare among contemporaneous responses to MacLane, the writer was a woman - Mrs. T.D. McKown (1869-?), until now lost to history.

The publisher - Inter-State Book Co., of Chicago - appears to have been a one-shot created for the purpose. The copyright filing bears the name

"E.A. Weeks," and the direction of inquiry this opens shows clear if still-distant shapes.

Weeks is a figure known to scholars of works by A. Conan Doyle, Thomas Hardy, James Whitcomb Riley, and others as a literary pirate, busily active as E.A. Weeks & Co. out of Chicago in the 1890s. He - about whom little is known outside of business - would brazenly pirate and file for copyright works by American and British writers to which he had no conceivable right. With no little cheek he dubbed one group of such thefts his "Enterprise" series, out of which emerge names of writers then-famed, now varyingly remembered: Anthony Hope, Leo Tolstoy (with *Master and Man*), Bertha N. Clay, Alexandre Dumas (*The Memoirs of a Physician*).

And yet, Weeks was not only a fraud. Scholars have commented on his books' fine production values - imitation laid paper, gilt edges, fine cover work - and *Letters* was in that line. The gold-yellow cover's red Satan holding a missive aloft has kept its color, and the curiously luxe top-gilt has kept a century's dust from fusing pages.

After dropping from the record about 1899, the publisher deigned speak to reporters about the new project, calling its author "a woman of high social standing in a Western state." After this, Weeks and his latest firm drop from the record - under, at any rate, those names.

The publicly-unnamed author was in reality Sarah H. McKown - her maiden name is still unknown. She was born in 1869 in Alabama, and in 1892 married Thomas D. McKown, a physician and sometime inventor from Chickamauga, Georgia. By 1897 the couple was in Cripple Creek, Colorado, and by 1904 at age 35 she was living in Denver apart from him. In 1908 they remarried in Georgia for unknown reasons (be it divorce, a defect in the original rite, or other); "McKown" is the name both used on the license. The 1910 census shows them dwelling together in a Georgia town close by the Tennessee border.

In 1912 she takes the job of Postmaster in nearby Pittsburg at the age of 43. In the mid-1910s her husband dies, and at this point she is lost to history. As far we know, she published nothing else and never spoke publicly about her one book.

*

The obvious is readily said. Mrs. McKown is no undiscovered great. She brings with her the clear expression inculcated in her time and an agreeable smatter of quotations of worthy sources. In her avoidance of prolix pomp she writes on the side of the moderns: steel pen instead of quill. She never slows our progress with fine airs or metaphors, and at few points is the reader detained in wonder or admiration.

What she brings is a sustained masquerade in which - for perhaps the first time - a female author, of apparent conventional morals and religiosity, adopts the persona of Satan with surprising assurance and gusto. Through dozens of entries the Devil commits or hints at the expected transgressions, but the written tone is anything but foreboding. That is kept for not-overconvincing comments to MacLane about how many converts she is winning for him by continuing on her course, etc.

When the Devil is just being the Devil he's having a simply grand time: relentless salesman, hypnotic seducer (necessarily quite the dancer), cross-dressing gender-switcher who invades the Woman's Club, regular exclaimer on the beauty of the female form. This, more than any parody of MacLane, is where the text has its independent being. In this text's world, MacLane dwindles. She is but an excuse.

Which adds a further layer: MacLane had asked in *Story/I Await* to be used - solely by the Devil himself. And McKown - not the Devil, but writing as him - came closest to obliging the desire.

Likely innocent of the implications, the safely anonymous Mrs. McKown commits an act of masked lesbian appropriation. As MacLane wrote some years after 1902, "so many [male] imitations of [the Devil] presented themselves, all with the one crude purpose, that he and his sometimes charm grew a bore and a monotony."

And so, the 34-year-old doctor's wife of Cripple Creek came perhaps closest to fulfilling MacLane's expressed fantasies. And that MacLane was at least varied in her sexual preferences adds a further luster of complication to the game of truths and masks.

*

A last strangeness.

Following the lead provided by the redoubtable Mr. Weeks, the only Mrs. T.D. McKown to be found in the western USA at that time is a woman in Colorado: president of a social club with 125 active members - the Cripple Creek Woman's Club. To a reader of *Letters*, this brings to mind two letters as one: the depiction of Cripple Creek's Fourth of July (the most colored, detailed, outer-facing entry) - and McKown's triply gender-flipped penetration of an unnamed town's Woman's Club.

These are the book's two most outward, specific entries - and it is at those very places we find Mrs. McKown in the historical record. That the

Club's entry is the Fourth of July's closest neighbor but one stands as a bow on the knot.

Now that MacLane's 1903 feature articles for the *Denver Post* have been recovered, McKown's motive in writing as she did - at four times the length of *Willie* or *Lizzie* - comes clearer.

MacLane's first article tartly describes a visit to a Woman's Club in Colorado Springs. It sets off the Club and the persons therein as a foreground that fades against the state's lasting natural background. Thus: "At Colorado Springs in the varnished hall I looked at women and considered them as was my bounden duty. There were all sorts there. All the sorts and conditions that go to make up the different types of the genus club-woman."

For all the lesbian bending that returns again and again in her text, McKown - writing very quickly, probably consciously turned to defend her morals, religion, and Colorado Springs sisters - likely never knew. But we can. For she turned us into voyeurs, too.

Did McKown and MacLane meet in the Colorado Springs hall? Did they have words? Is MacLane's MacLane using McKown's Devil? Is McKown's Devil using MacLane's MacLane? The standoff appears fixed and, at this very late date, perpetual.

Long may they glower!

Our post-moderns could make a fine industry in elaborating it all in their portable *pro tem* halls-of-mirrors.

All this, in a work written for that most devilish of motives - revenge! - and in the fun that's possible only through seriousness, which is possible only through fun.

Michael R. Brown
Butte County, California

THE DEVIL'S LETTERS TO MARY MACLANE

by Himself

[Mrs. T.D. McKown]

- 1903 -

To those before whose trembling lips
Is poised the cup of sin;
To those who, with enraptured eyes,
Behold the fleeting Paradise
That lurks within.

Dear Little Mary MacLane: -

I hope you will pardon my delay in replying to your very unusual and unexpected communication. I assure you that it was unavoidable. You must know that there are many and pressing demands upon me at all times.

To say that I was astounded at the nature of your message, but meagerly expresses it. As a rule, nothing ever astonishes me, but such a very extraordinary communication from a woman "of nineteen years and all alone," was a "corker" for even the Devil!

Really, Mary, you have over-acted your part.

Your book has turned out to be a regular "Methodist slop-over," like Deacon Gruntgander's prayer for rain. He sent up such a stirring appeal to Heaven, that the floodgates thereof were opened! "The winds blew, and the rains descended and the floods came," and washed away every remnant of vegetation for miles and miles around. One good sister said:

"They oughter a-knowed better'n to set Deacon Gruntgander a-prayin' fur rain. He never knows when to stop nuthin' he goes at, but keeps rite on till he slops clean over, every time."

You have something of Deacon Gruntgander's propensity, but let us hope that you haven't spoilt things entirely.

If you had sent the message to me privately, it would have been different; but to calmly, deliberately draw aside the curtains from both your treasure-house and your charnel-house door, and say to the rabble of the earth, "Behold!"

Devil as I am, I am amazed!

I can see your soul standing before you in utter nakedness, ready for its final crucifixion! I can see it fall on its knees and beg for mercy. I can see it weeping for the strands of gleaming pearls, which you have stripped from its white throat, and cast madly, ruthlessly before the swine of the earth! (The swine are now crunching them between their teeth for acorns. Ha!-ha!-ha!) I can see it stretch out its white arms to you in entreaty - and I can see you nail them pitilessly to the cross of Ignominy!

Truly, Mary, you are a wonder!

But there is one pearl - the largest, the most beautiful, the most wondrously white of all - which you did not cast with the others. You and your Soul have hidden it away somewhere. Did you think to fool me along with everyone else, when you claimed to have withheld nothing in your Portrayal?

I am surprised, Mary.

You are beginning to tremble and turn pale. You know very well which pearl I mean.

Is it possible that all my millions and millions of emissaries in the form of the man-devil have overlooked you entirely - you "of nineteen years and all alone!"

If so, I cannot blame you for sending up such a shriek.

Ah, Mary, what should you know about "strong steel arms, and wonderful burning kisses"? What should you know about being "consumed with hot love;" and your "soul and the soul of the man-devil meeting in an anguish of joy"?

I have not been to you personally, because I felt sure of you. I give my individual attention to only the pure, white-souled ones who otherwise would escape me. Sometimes they slip through my fingers in spite of all my endeavors - as did the soul of Marguerite!

When I saw that beautiful thing, purged to dazzling whiteness, borne heavenward, I felt my throne totter under me! Hell was rent by a convulsion that almost laid it in twain! I fell prostrate on my face, smitten with blindness, while heavy thunders rolled over me! The lake parted in the middle, and there arose from my imps such a "wailing and gnashing of teeth," that the very ramparts of Heaven were shaken!

Is there such a possibility for you?

Ah, no, Mary!

That bitter wound alone, which you gave the mother-heart, has made you mine indissolubly! "For I am persuaded, that neither death, nor life, nor angels, nor principalities, nor powers, nor things present, nor things to come, nor height, nor depth, nor any other creatures, shall be able to separate" you from the dominion of the Devil!

Oh, that poor mother! I am minded, Devil as I am, to stop and weep for her. To think that the little hand, which the mysterious forces within her body wrought into being, should have lived to give her such a thrust!

From the depths of my metal heart, I pity her!

What is it that is sharper than a serpent's tooth?

Isn't it a thankless child?

Indeed you are a genius, Mary - a genius of unkindness!

But here I am moralizing. Ha!-ha!-ha!

Yours in astonishment,
THE DEVIL.

*

My Astonishing Mary: -

Well! What is the Devil to expect of you next?

I no more than collect my wits to declare myself unto you than you burst forth with another effusion.

Of course I am interested in all that concerns you, but to be honest and frank, your friend, Annabel Lee, is too tame for me. I am not specially interested in her at the present, but in you, Mary - the Mary of your Portrayal - who are the living embodiment of feminine mystery. The next time you come, Mary, leave our friend Annabel Lee at home.

Your impatient,
DEVIL.

*

My Incomparably Egotistical Mary: -
The night is ended.
I am alone.
My secret emissaries, that come and go at my volition, are all on duty bound. That vague, unbroken communication which they establish between me and my votaries, has revealed to me through the medium of your Portrayal, the virtues and the follies of yourself.

Reveling as I am in the spoils of my conquests, I am nevertheless impressed with the fervor of your communication, but amused - nay, provoked - with its absurdity; and when I seek to analyze the meaning of your weird, uncanny purpose to serve me, I almost hesitate to trust you. I am somewhat irritated over the fact that you have laid bare your soul - exposed both its faults and virtues in such an unguarded manner, and I am forced to question it.

Is the message which you have sent me the well-timed, well-tuned phrasing of a willing subject, or the mutterings of a diseased brain, that "knows no distinction 'twixt" God and the Devil?

Was that mountain of selfishness, hatred, idiosyncrasies, ever created in the image of God? Was that perversion of all that is attractive even to the Devil, ever moulded by the hand of the Creator? Does the spirit of life burn with a steady flame, or does it flicker through the mutilations of a dethroned reason?

Even the Devil scorns to engage the irresponsible.

The wonderful genius with which you, Mary MacLane, imagine yourself to be burdened, the Devil fails to recognize.

You have written a book!

You have given this book to the world, and it is now the property of the world.

What is it? and what of you, Mary MacLane, who produced it?

You have strung together a few slang phrases from Hell, a little worn-out philosophy from Heaven, a miserable compound of earth, and imagine that you have produced the work of a genius.

It is studded, I grant you, with literary gems; and the sentences are touched with a finish that is exquisite in the extreme. What you have said, you have said cleverly; and even I must admit that you have said some clever things.

I do not deplore the fact that you have prostituted to my cause the talent that was given to you for a higher purpose; but rather rejoice in the careless abandon with which you enter into the spirit of my undertakings.

You have robbed me of some of my most characteristic sentiments, and have clothed them in a language of exquisite beauty and purity. You have given to a rosary of black diamonds a setting of pearls. The world, now, will see only the black diamonds; but when the glamour of criticism with which it is enshrouded shall have passed away, the pearls will be revealed.

It is not with pearls that I have to deal; for pearls, even literary pearls, are not of my kingdom.

While the name of Mary MacLane is on the lips of every one, it is only just and natural that the Devil, to whom your most earnest pleas are addressed, should communicate to you his sentiments regarding yourself.

In speaking of your genius, I do not depreciate the fact that your work is a clever one; but neither the world nor the Devil would consider it the product of the mighty genius that you persist in calling yourself. The Devil is something of a genius himself, and he protests against having the term so misapplied. Even he feels outraged at the audacity of a morbid, morose, peripatetic, world-despising creature, who essays to masquerade under the crown of genius.

Devil that I am, I would not rise up and declare that none were devilish but myself. I have wit enough to see that there are others who apply the Devil's tactics quite as gracefully, and almost as effectually, as he does himself. Many of my pupils have threatened to outstrip their tutor - although the world knows that neither Heaven nor earth has ever produced but the one Devil.

I am proud, but I am not boastful.

I established my claims to my unique sovereignty before I asserted them. You, little Mary MacLane, have boldly said to the world: "*I am a genius!*" and your sole justification for the assertion seems to be the fact that you have stated it.

Does it take a genius to lay hold of the infinite guile of the Devil, and to present it in terse, clear, epigrammatic language for the edification of those who haven't the ability to evolve it for themselves? Is the stern manner in which you have stated facts, the rounded periods in which you have exalted your own virtues, the pathos that you have inserted into a recital of unre-

lenting truths, the melody that you have wrung from nature's c
tyranny of love that you have painted so glowingly, the climax c
that you have drawn so vividly, the work of a genius?

The Devil looks beyond all this - looks through your work at the hand
that wrought it. He deals, not with the pen-picture of your "wooden heart,"
but with the human heart that is swayed by sentiments in which the Devil
exults. He does not analyze, nor expatiate upon the pathetic beauty and
the mute eloquence with which you melt the hearts of your readers over
the conditions of your loveless life; but rather reflects upon the cold, selfish
existence that has made your life a natural consequence.

I do not deny the fact that you have talent, neither do I deplore it; but
I am amused, nevertheless, at the unsophisticated manner in which you
assert your egotism and proclaim your genius.

An egotist you are!

No one would disclaim your right to call yourself a puny, presuming,
self-created egotist; but I fancy that you overrate the importance which even
that distinction might accord you.

The barn-yard cock looks with contempt upon the pin-feathered, crow-
ing rooster. The animals of the forest treat with merited disapproval the
insolence of their young, which rise to confront them with the fact that
there is no danger abroad, because they themselves have explored the world
as far as the brow of the hill.

The busts of the sages will not turn their wizened heads to view the advent
of a new genius. The busy, rushing world will not pause long to contemplate
the light of your reigning glory. The sun and moon will not waver in their
orbits because of a counter attraction. In the face of your marvelous egotism,
the fixed star will still remain the centre of the universe!

The mind that sent forth this rumbling, sporadic effort bears the same
relation to genius that the bubbling fountain bears to the roaring cataract.

Genius is great!

The world recognizes it without a label. It rides its majestic course unchallenged, and sweeps through the firmament of existence with the calm
security of its position. There is no bickering after Fame - that awkward,
unmanageable, reflected attachment to the star of greatness. Genius is never
seen, booted and spurred, "valiantly astride a charger riding down the world,
with Fame following at the charger's heels, and the multitude agape."

Genius is its own glory!

There is no relapse of genius into the qualms of its own intensity. Genius
stands appalled at the audacity with which you assert your claims to genius.

You are young, but the world is old; and I am older yet than either.

I have watched the course of genius, as it played in iridescent beauty above the horizon; rose in the magnificent splendor of a glorious noon; then sank, as the western sun, behind a gorgeous setting!

The path of genius is not deflected. It runs its course according to the limitations of its fixed orbit; and not through the wabbling peregrinations of a satellite.

Your brilliant metaphors and your rhetorical cadences have a worthy significance, which even the Devil does not wholly disregard; but it is the vicious serpent, coiled within this flower of perfect English, that challenges the Devil.

The world might forgive your youthful audacity, had that been your only sin; but when you put up your body and soul for auction, and bid them in for the Devil, the world leaves you with the auctioneer, and the Devil has only to claim you for his Own.

So cheaply bought, you may expect to be cheaply prized; and if there be no other use to which you may be applied, I can, at least, make a plaything of you.

Yours deploringly,
THE DEVIL.

*

My Precocious Little Saga: -

Your peripatetic philosophy has made you wise beyond your years. In contrast to the simpering idiocy of youth, you are propounding to yourself such serious questions as, "What would I do if the earth were made of wood with a paper sky?"

This is too weighty a problem for the Devil, but I would caution you in a case like that, not to hurl any more such brands as you did in your Portrayal, or you might set the whole thing on fire, and get to Hell before your time!

You have said you never were "that quaint conceit, a girl -"

> *Standing with reluctant feet,*
> *Where the brook and river meet.*

No; you straddled over all that, Mary.

You never knew the incomparable bliss of *giggling*!

You never experienced the ecstatic joy of a wad of chewing-gum, nor the unspeakable pleasure of a street-corner beau. You never knew the thrill of exchanging girlish confidences, nor tasted the supreme beatitude of a girl's first love-letter.

Above all, you never felt the transport of an engagement ring on your finger!

You looked beyond all this.

In your Portrayal, you exclaim rapturously:

"When my happiness is given me, life will be an ineffable, a nameless thing.

"It will seethe and roar; it will plunge and whirl; it will leap and shriek in convulsion; it will quiver in delicate fantasy; it will writhe and twist; it will glitter and flash and shine; it will sing gently; it will shout in exquisite excitement; it will vibrate to the roots like a great oak in a storm; it will dance; it will glide; it will gallop; it will rush; it will swell and surge; it will fly; it will soar high - high; it will go down into depths unexplored; it will rage and rave; it will yell in utter joy; it will melt; it will blaze; it will ride triumphant; it will grovel in the dust of entire pleasure; it will sound out like a terrific blare of trumpets; it will chime faintly, faintly like the remote tinkling notes of a harp; it will sob and grieve and weep; it will revel and carouse; it will shrink; it will go in pride; it will lie prone like the dead; it will float buoyantly on air; it will moan, shiver, burst - oh, it will reek with Love and Light!"

Your description is marvelous, but, as you say, wholly inadequate.

Though I am the Prince of Liars, I swear to you that when your happiness comes, life will be a chaotic, an intangible, a nondescript thing!

It will boil and sizzle; it will bound and lunge; it will jump and howl and fall in a fit; it will bubble, and spurt geysers of liquefied madness; it will wriggle; it will squirm; it will twinkle and glow and burn; it will whistle rhapsodies through its teeth; it will purr; it will scream and screech and bellow like a bull; it will buzz softly, softly; it will shake to its marrow bones; it will hop; it will skip; it will lope; it will shout; it will warble; it will spread its wings; it will hump itself up - up; it will rip and rave; it will snort and foam at the mouth; it will rear; it will charge; it will buck like a broncho; it will wallow in the sloughs of delight; it will tinkle shrilly, shrilly like the echo of a brass cow-bell; it will wail; it will wring its hands; it will tear its hair; it will grit its teeth; it will squeal like a pig under a gate; it will prance and cavort; it will scamper; it will dance like a flea with the colic; it will fall on its face; it will cleave the air like a Thomas (cat) orchestra by night; it will sigh, groan, "*bust*" - oh, it will scintillate comets and shooting-stars!

With "wonderful burning kisses,"
Yours ecstatically,
THE DEVIL.

*

My Impatient, Expectant Mary: -

I too am growing impatient, Mary - impatient for the hour when I may claim you as my own - my bride for a season - (Oh, rapturous thought!)

I am the most adorable of lovers, little girl; and the hour in which you fall under the spell of my fascination, you will count all else as an empty bauble.

My heart, like a drunken Bacchus, would fain forget the duties which lie nearest, and fly at once to that haven of bliss to which you have invited me.

My kisses, little girl (and I have the most bewitching manner of bestowing them), are all that a "woman, young and alone," could wish.

There is something potently magical in the devil's kisses; something irresistible, overwhelming in its entirety; something that disarms the halting soul, and lays it prostrate at my feet.

God, himself, gave me this power, and God has not removed his creatures beyond temptation. (Ha!-ha!-ha!)

I am no moralist, Mary, and when I come to clasp you in my strong steel arms, to pour out to you the passionate adoration of my metal heart, and to bewilder you with the ecstasy of the Devil's hot kisses, there shall be no hint of direful consequences.

No! I shall love you in my own way; love you; *love you*; LOVE YOU! Yes, I shall love you, in my *own way*. (Ha!-ha!-ha!)

Yours, adoringly,
THE DEVIL.

*

My Strangely Pathetic Child: -

You, little Mary MacLane, from the depths of your loneliness and gloom, have pictured the personality of the Devil.

Your youth and uncurbed fancy have made him more a god than the wily, crafty, world-defiling Devil that he is. You have given him attributes that ill become the sovereign of Hell; and have laid bare a soul, the inner workings of which he would himself do well to imitate.

Come, little girl, pass before the throne of my judgment.

At first I see you, a trembling, untaught child, groping about in a wilderness of untamed nature; peering into the caverns that yawn at your feet; gazing over the precipice that leaps before your way, and straining your ears to catch the ripple of a fountain that plays in idle sport upon the peaceful plot below.

I watch you, as, with one little sun-burned hand, you clutch the barren crags for support; while, with the other, grasping the moss and lichens that cling among the rocks, you strive to pluck the flowers that grow beyond your reach.

Now you are startled by the raven's croak, and lift your wondering eyes to the bird that flies languidly across your skies. Then your vision is caught by the mesmeric charm of the serpent, as it winds its slender, iridescent body in serpentine grace before you; and, enchanted, you wonder at its beauty, and would seize it if you could.

When I contemplate you thus, my heart is filled with pity.

Again, you rise before me as a wild unruly element, that chafes at the restraint which nature has placed around you.

You challenge the wind as it sweeps past you, and would stay the mad cataract as it leaps in wild delight. In roguish pleasure you would rob the robin of her little blue eggs; and would torture the toad as it hops across your path. You would strip the flowers of their delicate petals, and would mock the whip-poor-will as it sings at dusk.

When I see you thus, and in willful petulance, knocking at the gate of the Unknown I am seized with a desire to chastise you, and to chastise you heroically.

Again, I see you at the early morn, waking, as it were, from a dream. You rise in all the beauty of youth, refreshed by sleep, and gaze with rapture at the dawn, as it blushes above the horizon. You contemplate the wonderful world around you, and look in admiration at nature, sparkling with the dews of Heaven.

Your wondering soul peers outward, and all is harmony and peace; inward - and all is mystery and doubt.

You lie down, stretch your limbs upon the ground, drink in the exquisite perfume from the garden of the universe, and revel in the intoxication of nature's dawn. You close your eyes, and give yourself up entirely to this rare, uncertain, unconscious bewilderment.

When I see you thus, I am constrained to force myself upon your dreams.

Again, you are roused from your idle slumber by a flood of hot, yellow sunlight.

The dawn has passed, and you wake to realize that the bright warm glow of womanhood has stirred you into life and energy.

You long to encompass the world and bend it to your fiery fancy.

You call humanity from its lethargy, and proclaim the fact that you have awakened!

You are filled with a furious desire to measure the flood of your emotions with the length and breadth of creation.

The infinity of time and space is pitifully small in comparison with the magnitude of your soul.

You pant; you rave; you exult in the heat of your passion. You beat against your barriers as a small bird might flutter against the wires of its cage. You leap; you plunge, with the paroxysms of a restrained vitality; then lapse into an infinite dream of happiness!

When I see you thus, I love you; and would take you to my breast and unfold to you the mysteries of life!

Your soul cries out in a passion of prayer:

"Why does the red never fail to come to the breast of the robin? Why does the sand and barrenness lie stretched out before me? Why does the moon stand in the sky, night after night? Why do the mountains and valleys live on as the years pass; and the marsh, and the mint and white hawthorn freeze over in the fall?"

You would know the "all-why" of things, Mary.

It is a pity that you should have been fretting your young life out, over these seemingly unsolvable problems, when the Devil could so easily have answered them for you.

The red comes to the breast of the robin because it would not be becoming on his tail; the sand and barrenness lie stretched out before you, because they cannot get up and walk; the moon stands in the sky, night after night, because it has nowhere else to stand; the mountains and valleys live on as the years pass, because they cannot die; the marsh, and the mint and white hawthorn freeze over in the fall, because the weather is cold.

Again I see you, after the first flood of fiery youth has spent itself, and the pulse of your temperament has assumed its normal condition.

You no longer rush madly into the vortex of youth's whirlpool, but steer your course into the deep channel, whose current is ever in one direction. You no longer yield without question to the intensity of your emotions, nor follow the rainbow of hallucination; but analyze your passions and propensities, adjust them to the world, and prepare to take your place in the ranks of those who have a turbulent nature to control.

When I see you thus I am seized with a desire to tempt you; ay, to persecute you, until you yield yourself to me without reserve.

When I see you, "young and all alone," walking in the path of conventionality, looking upon the world demurely and complacently from behind your armor of maidenhood - I approve of you, and laugh at the world's credulity.

When I see you stalk forth with the self-imposed consciousness of your egotism - I am amused.

When you stretch out your hand to the world, in mute supplication for love, and receive only a reprimand - I rebuke you for your weakness.

When you curse the world and all its ties and scoff at the thought of purity and truth - I am infinitely pleased with you.

When you measure your genius with that of, not only the world, but the Devil also - I am seized with a desire to ridicule you.

When you expose, despite the protestations of decency, the hot, seething passion that nature has bequeathed to you - I applaud you.

When you hesitate, and for a moment question the possibility of the truth, and long to believe the story of God's love and atonement - I despise you.

But when you surrender yourself fully and freely to the Devil; and ask of him only that he love you, and bring you to the rare, exquisite, intoxicating elixir of that love - I love you most, and glorify you (in the Devil's way).

While you are a creature of many moods, I am a creature of more.

I shall deal with your various moods in my own way; and before I have finished, little girl, you may know me better than you know me today!

Yours introspectively,
THE DEVIL.

*

Dear Little MacLane: -

You say that there are several things in life for which you "of womankind and nineteen years," have conceived a forcible repugnance. There are many things in the world for which I, the Kind Devil, have conceived a more forcible repugnance.

First of all: From homely women: Good God, deliver me.

From early-to-bedders and early-to-risers; from boy-choirs and hymn-tunes; from high collars; from nick-names: Good God, deliver me.

From hen-pecked husbands; from trick-babies; from female politicians; from boarders who give themselves "airs;" from appendicitis, Good God, deliver me.

From missionaries with tall hats who lecture on the Holy Land; from course dinners; from people who sweat; from slop-pails; from a "kid" with the hose; from flowers clutched in the hands of corpses: Good God, deliver me.

From homes where grace is said; from bad teeth; from bad breath; from the man who spits; from doting mothers with unspeakable children, who make long visits to relations: Good God, deliver me.

From little-faced women with huge pompadours; from church-bells; from frayed and knotted shoe-laces; from ping-pong; from newly married couples: Good God, deliver me.

From people with "pedigrees" (present company always excepted, Mary);

from bow-legged men; from Salvation Army bonnets; from bare feet, especially if they be gnarled with corns and bunions; from a "bigoty nigger": Good God, deliver me.

From shoes that squeak as one walks; from undertakers; from bed-bugs; from women who are never together in the back; from spectacled "kids;" from boiled cabbage (bah!): Good God, deliver me.

From designing mothers with marriageable daughters; from people who do not use tooth-brushes; from religious young men; from bargain sales: Good God, deliver me.

From the woman who travels with a section of hand-baggage; from association with the aged; from large hats at an opera house; from chewing-gum girls; from fat men in checker-board trousers; from "fee" waiters: Good God, deliver me.

From a "true story" novel (it is like a preserve with a pill in it); from peroxide blondes; from the man with schemes; from family prayers; from telephones; from poor relations: Good God, deliver me.

From celebrities in wax; from monocles; from women whose "pugs" and sailor hats do not make connection; from people who say "I seen, I done, had went, and hadn't ought to": Good God, deliver me.

From protracted meetings; from artificial flowers in the hair; from toy drums; from kid-curlers; from widows, by God, who are just emerging from second mourning, and widows, by grass, under all circumstances: Good God, deliver me.

From lisping young men with prodigious bouquets in their button-holes; from pimply complexions; from cold baths; from the refractory lock on a woman's neck which refuses to affiliate with the rest of her back hair, from "geniuses:" Good God, deliver me.

From folding beds; from philanthropists; from fine-tooth combs; from unsophisticated young girls who play the piano; from people who eat onions; from honest preachers; from nursing-bottles: Good God, deliver me.

From zealous females who sell tickets to church fairs; from bangle bracelets; from quill tooth-picks; from bland old gentlemen who marry and bury wives periodically: Good God, deliver me.

From young men who waltz irrespective of their partners; from shoes with tacks in them; from tight-laced women; from mouths that droop at the corners; from Mrs. Snobbs who does not speak to Mrs. So-and-So; from cold suppers; from stockings with holes in them; from sour pickles (they give me the lockjaw): Good God, deliver me.

From the "Is-this-hot-enough-for-you" fiend (I'll get it back on him some day); from round shoulders; from "wall-flowers;" from burial robes; from the old maid with "views:" Good God, deliver me.

From men who wear their neckties under their left ears; from back-door neighbors; from sour-faced school-marms; from anemone ladies; from fleeing Josephs, who leave their vestments in the hands of a Potiphar's wife (there are such, Mary): Good God, deliver me.

From that rare confection, the "debutante;" from straight-backed chairs; from soiled linen; from old women in decolette gowns; from sewing societies; from would-be authors; from people who "work" their friends; from a woman with a dust cap and a broom; from fools: Good God, deliver me.

From prudish old maids at the sea-shore; from soiled kid gloves, and gloves out at the fingers; from the woman who eschews dress-shields; from Sunday school books; from the sight of old Jack Martin on horseback: Good God, deliver me.

From the rear view of a woman who wears run-down shoes and the "kangaroo hump" - oh! from the rear view of a woman who wears run-down shoes and the "kangaroo hump:" Good God, deliver me.

Mary, oh! Mary, don't ever wear that combination, and turn your back to -
THE DEVIL.

P.S. - Many of the above agencies I am compelled to employ in my business, but no one abominates them more than I.

THE D--L.

*

Poor Lonely Mary MacLane: -

The barrenness of your childhood!

You cry out against it - and no wonder!

Ah! yes; the barrenness of childhood, in some instances, is a calamity which even I blush to admit.

The omnipotent Creator has left his work unguarded; and it is an easy matter for the Devil to breathe upon the future even of an unborn child, and wither into desolation all the influences which might, at least, add beauty and variety to its condition.

The poor little unfortunates are born into my sphere. They are mine by inheritance; and I probably neglect to make their condition as roseate with color and amusement, as I have made the paths of those of maturer years.

The joys of my kingdom are not for children; and I often regret that I cannot supply, from my abundance, the aching void of a lonely childhood.

The little lives that struggle into this world through pain and hardship; lives which have fallen in stony places, and sucked their bare sustenance from the overflow of a more favored spot; lives that cast their little tendrils out, but find nothing on which to fasten them; lives that are strangers to the beauty and tenderness of love, because they are rooted on the bleak hillside where the benign breezes of sympathy and affection do not pass; lives that are twisted and dwarfed by the chilling blasts to which they are exposed; lives whose early dews and fragrance have been swept away in the very immensity of their surroundings - little lives like these are such that even I do not rejoice in.

My work is not among these, although I often hear their pitiful plea for love, and see their little hearts dwarfed and twisted for lack of that which is their birthright - and for which the world is languishing. I have looked into their little pinched faces and read the stony glare of a hungry soul, and found the tell-tale traces of early disappointments.

I could weep - yes I, the Devil - at conditions which force them into the ranks of my followers before their little minds can grasp the magnitude of my service. Even *I* contend that a child has a right to be happy; and those who deny children this privilege defraud the Devil of much of his glory. Poor little Mary MacLane! You were a seed that fell in a stony place! Were there no sweet haunts in nature, in whose solitude you might have buried your loneliness? no childhood sports that might have lured you to forget your desolation?

Was there, for you, no beauty in the flowers of the field, the blue of the sky, and the stars of the midnight heavens? Did your childish imagination never picture the spirit-hand that painted the rosy dawn, silvered the evening moon, and curved the ribbons of the rainbow?

Heard you no music in the twitter of the birds, in the sobbing of the pines, and in the whisper of the sea-shell? Found you no friends in the laughing waters of the brook! nor kind companions in the quaint tones of the echo? Were you never filled with awe at the magnificence of the lightning, and the sullen grandeur of the thunder?

Did you never people the clouds with fairies, and imagine yourself queen of their wonderful realm? Did the butterflies, with their spangled wings, never come to you as to other children, like visitants from an unknown world of mystery and light? Did nature offer you no companions save weeds, and lizards, and snakes?

Nature's rare harmonies, to which your childish sense seems to have been utterly dead, are the works of the Omnipotent which I have never been able to mar. The infinite beauty which they pour into the lives of children is often the most lasting influence which I have to encounter in later years. Did you pass through the ways of childhood impervious to such influences? Then, poor little Mary MacLane, you are an easy prey to the Devil!

Yours sympathetically,
THE DEVIL.

*

Oh Mary: -

How could you write a Portrayal in a stiff-backed chair? I could not even eat hot fudge, or hold my best girl on my knee, in one.

If I call on a woman, and she seats me in a stiff-backed chair, I don't stop long.

Yours luxuriously,
THE DEVIL.

*

My Rampant Peripatetic Mary: -

And is it happiness that you seek, little MacLane?

Happiness!

A strange thing to ask at my hands!

It is not the lost happiness of childhood that you seek (or you would never have come to me), but the rich, luscious portion that the Devil offers to buoyant youth.

What though the red and gold of the sunset change to leaden grey?

What though the bronze and copper beams on the three white rocks fade into deep shadows?

What though the happiness I bring you be only for three days, one day, *an hour*, it is supreme while it lasts - while it lasts!

You have said that for one single hour of Happiness you would give up "Fame, and Money, and Power, and Virtue, and Honor, and Righteousness, and Truth, and Logic, and Philosophy, and Genius."

I can give you, in exchange for all these, a feast that will melt your sensibilities into a dream!

The emptiness of your life that has almost crushed you with its very nothingness, I can fill to the full limit of your limitless soul!

I robbed Paradise of its bliss, and it is with this that I can steep your senses in mad intoxication! Yes, I can pour into your soul that for which it longs, and sway your spirit with that wild delirium for which men have ever bartered their souls!

Under the "red, red light" of the Devil's love, the mysteries of life that have been hidden in the bleak barren waste of Nothingness shall unfold at the touch of a new inspiration! Those tender, blushing petals shall expand to meet the measure of their counterpart, and shall shed their fragrance around the couch of your awakening I The bleak sordidness of your life, I can illumine with the brilliancy of a revelation!

Come, little Mary MacLane, and sit down to my feast.

Come, in the buoyancy of health, life, and spirit.

Bring no regrets.

Stifle the voice which might protest against the bartering of your all for Happiness. Bury the little germ of womanhood which might have lodged in the breast of even *you*. Let there be no whisper from the Past that might awaken in your heart a sigh for other days - no echo from the lamentation of a soul sold into bondage!

Let there be no skeleton at the Devil's feast.

Come! I am waiting to lead you to the feast of Happiness, where none may deny my right to unfold to you the weird seductions of my kingdom; where the "red, red light" is but an enchanting glow from the never-dying flames of Hell!

Many, before you, have been lured to my feast by this wonderful, roseate glamour!

Come, drink deep at the fountain of youthful intoxication!

Come, in the fullness of your "young woman's body!"

Come, with your "wooden heart" on fire!

Come, with your "red, red blood flowing swiftly and joyously!"

Come, with your "sound, sensitive liver resting gently with its thin yellow bile in sweet content!"

Come, dancing to the music of your "beautiful stomach, singing its song of peace."

Come, with your "strong, sensitive nerves reeking and swimming in sensuality like little drunken Bacchantes."

Come, on your "two good legs" to my feast.

Come! I am waiting for you in "the slow-deepening dusk" - with a butt of olives.

With all the love of my metal heart-Ha!-ha!!-ha!!!

I am yours rapturously,
THE DEVIL

*

My Own Mary: -

The hour is long past midnight.

The morning star, that has watched through the night, is sinking toward the western horizon, while its myriad companions are fading into the limitless light of dawn.

My labors through the night have been as varied as they have been unceasing. I have visited the halls of revelry and song.

I have sat down at the banquet feast of princes. I have thrown a deeper cloud of disappointment around the hovels of the poor. I have visited anew the sick and suffering, and have poured a little more discontent into the hearts of the blind and crippled. I have dazzled the unwary with temptation, and have drawn others more securely into my coils. I have visited the grogshops and the dives of sin, and have caused God's creatures to blaspheme His holy name.

At the magic hour of midnight, when revelry was at its height, I entered the brilliant halls of the masquerade, and danced with the queen of the ball.

The impersonation of Night, she was: swathed in filmy black, with the crescent moon on her brow. Her eyes, from behind her mask, gleamed like midnight stars, and

Her snow-white breasts were springing,
Like fountains, 'neath her veil.

I folded her to my heart, and her form seemed melted into mine, as we floated away on the wings of the dreamful waltz, her star-bespangled draperies enveloping us like a cloud!

Oh, it is something to be the Devil, after all!

To be king, for a season, with all the rank and file of humanity only waiting for an opportunity to serve me!

Poor fools that they are!

They do not know with what little compunction I dazzle them, and then cheat them of their inheritance.

What does it matter?

This is the Devil's reign, and I propose to reign right royally!

I can lead my army of weak, cowardly, self-debased, devil-despised vagabonds into the very shadow of Hell, and they do not desert me. They may waver for a while, but they eventually fall in with the mass, and follow up a course which they know has but one ultimatum.

Occasionally there are deserters - those who turn back into the "straight and narrow way." To be honest with myself (the Devil must be that; he may lie to the world, but he must be honest with himself), the numerous desertions are becoming alarming.

It does not argue well for my vigilance.

It foreshadows the time when the Prince of Peace shall reign in my stead.

I must visit the great tabernacles, which stand like conscious and ever-watchful sentinels; I must shadow those who enter and those who leave; I must encompass them with the network of my subtlety.

Could I but ensnare the shepherds of those flocks, the sheep might then wander away; and, though I might not be able to recover the entire fold, many, in their confusion would undoubtedly drift into my ranks.

So, I say to myself, "Away, good Devil! You have no time for ease and comfort. The luxurious surroundings of your throne must not tempt you into lethargy."

You, little Mary MacLane, who rest securely in the fold of Satan, I must leave for a while, and direct my attention to those who might possibly escape me.

I can only say to you:

"Continue to nurse the morbidness of your nature, and to rebel against your natural surroundings; hate the mother who gave you being; bring her grey hairs down in sorrow to the grave; curse the memory of your father; cast a spell of contamination over all who know you, and honor the Devil by exercising in his behalf the talent that has been lent you.

"Lie, steal, vilify yourself and others; and dream of the 'red, red light' of your happiness - until I come."

And when I come, may I find no fault in you!

Yours in delay,
THE DEVIL.

*

My Artful Little Mary: -

Ha!-ha!-ha!! You are a sly one, Mary.

The joke is on the Devil this time.

He is masculine enough to have had his curiosity aroused by your frequent allusions to your "young woman's body," and feminine enough to wish to gratify that curiosity.

Now, Mary, the Devil is an autocrat on the subject of physical beauty - especially the beauty of a woman's form.

The Creator certainly did a magnificent piece of work when he made the physical woman!

No one has a keener appreciation of woman's beauty than have I.

I know what constitutes the acme of perfection - what curves and contours lend the most enchanting grace.

I love to revel in the contemplation of her charms - the rounded cheek, where roses blush at the kiss of perfect health; lips, as red as the wild wind-flower, that sprang from the blood of dying Adonis; eyes that gaze into mine from the infinite blue depths of the firmament, or melt my soul with the warmth of their Egyptian darkness; soft, magnetic hands and dimpled arms, that far "outmatch the sculptor's dreaming;" a throat of matchless purity; and a bosom that heaves and swells with the exultation of youth and love.

Ay! I love to force myself still further into her privacy, and study the slender waist and the magnificent development of the limbs, whose tapering lines are culminated in the slender ankles, that ill-suggest the full proportions they support.

Lucky Devil that I am!

There are few dressing-rooms that I do not enter.

I linger in the silken folds of draperies, and hide in the network of lace that serves as lingerie. I smile from the jewels that sparkle on a bare bosom, or mount the tiara that scintillates with myriad gems.

I lurk in the diaphanous train, as it plays in idle sport with the delicately arched instep. I play hide-and-seek behind her fan, and coil in the fragrant petals of the rose, as it dies upon her breast.

Yes, woman I love - and woman I love to flatter.

I won the queen of Paradise through flattery, and I still pursue her daughters.

Woman was created to be loved, to be petted, to be flattered; and when man fails to do his duty in this respect, it is an easy matter for the Devil to supplant him. If a woman has a beautiful face, a perfect form, or an inherent grace, and her rightful lord neglects to show his appreciation of nature's kind bestowals, the Devil is sure to tell her.

You, Mary, with the characteristic archness of your sex, have told the Devil about your "two good legs," and have had so much to say about the perfection of your "young woman's body" - although you did confess to the cunning distribution of "nine cambric handkerchiefs" and the dextrous arrangement of a "striped moreen petticoat" - that he decided to pay you a visit.

Accordingly, he perched himself on the top of the "low bureau," on which you prop your feet to eat fudge, and read "Our Young Folks" (pardon me; I do not mean that you prop your feet on the top of it), and watched the disrobing scene.

The Devil is no mischievous tattle-tale.

He will not tell what he saw - but he was disappointed!

Yours, not to be fooled,
THE DEVIL.

*

Oh! Rash Little Child: -

You, with the witchery of your sex have dared to flirt with Death!

Death, Death! that weird, grand, magnificent demonstration of my power! The final victory, which it is my privilege to wring from those who have obeyed my precepts, as well as from those who have hearkened unto the gentle importunities of the Prince of Peace!

You, in your youthful audacity, have dared to flirt with *Death*!

Death, Death! the fell destroyer, that

Sweeps the lines where beauty lingers!

Death, Death! that dulls the quick ear, clouds the soulful eye, and sets the eternal seal of silence on lips that erst were full of song!

Death, Death! that dark, uncanny spirit of my realm, that knows no age, no sex, no limitations! Who snatches the tender babe from its mother's breast with as little compunction as it fans out the flickering flame of age!

You, who are but as the dust that clings to the measure of an omnipotent ruling, have speculated upon the surrender of yourself to Death! You, who know not whence you came, nor whither you go, but only that you are - *you* have dared to tempt that power before whose omnipotence even *I* shall quail!

Have you, little Mary MacLane, ever thought upon what a slender cord your life suspends? who gave it - and for what purpose?

In your wild enthusiasm, you probably attribute to me greater power than I possess.

I can mar, I can destroy; but I cannot restore.

That vague, intangible mystery of life which has been breathed into the universe itself, even I have failed to grasp.

I can wreak destruction upon the face of nature; but I cannot rebuild it. I can snuff out the subtle flame of life; but -

I know not where is that Promethean fire
That can its light relume.

Have you never, with any feeling of uncertainty, fancied what death might mean to you?

Picture to yourself a frail pleasure boat, cut from its moorings, and with sails set to the breeze, driven out upon an unknown sea. Will it drift forever in the calm security of a beneficent Providence? or will it follow the "red, red light" of an alluring deity, and rush to utter destruction upon either the Scylla or Charybdis which I have created to ensnare the unwary?

Yes, little Mary MacLane, you may flirt with Death! You may taunt him with your waywardness, may dazzle him with the glory of life; but, in due time, the blackness of night shall envelop you - and Death shall claim his own!

Again, I say, flirt with Death!

Tantalize this wizened monarch with the captivating joys of youth.

Array your beauty in its most resistless garb; inspire him with the witchery of your smiles; dazzle him with the beauty of your form; intoxicate him with the nectar of your lips!

He may not linger at your side long enough now to blight those charms with which you tempt him; but the time will come when he will surely wrap you in a shroud of eternal darkness!

That cheek, whereon is painted the ruddy glow of health, shall moulder and decay. Those eyes, within whose depths the fire of youth is kindled, shall dim beneath a misty shroud. Those lips, dipped, as it were, in carmine of the sunset - those lips that part with the mystery of life and love - shall crumble into dust!

That "young woman's body," in its exquisite beauty and symmetry of form, shall become the habitation of worms; and the spirit that it is tenanted with shall take its flight to -

The undiscovered country, from whose bourn
No traveler returns.

To the earthly record of Mary MacLane shall be appended those fateful words - THE END!

Again, I say, flirt with Death, if you will.

At best, it can only be for a season.

The grim old reaper of Time knows no distinction between thistles and wheat.

Stretch out your limbs upon the ground; drink in the beauty of the grey dawn; revel in the rich, warm glow of the noonday sun: and grow melancholy in the soft, purple tints of the sunset - for the night will surely come when all will be lost in shadow!

Flirt with Death!

For when the harvest of Time shall have claimed you, poor little Mary MacLane, your unmeasured egotism, your incomparable intensity, your mountain of genius (?), your "young woman's body" will cut a very small figure in the domain of the Devil!

The fancied flights of genius, through which your morbid imagination leads you, will then prove to be the promptings of an idiosyncratic mind and an immoral heart.

The great genius (?) that rose to cast forth its mutterings against "the stupid old world," and communicated its low, sordid, baleful, vicious iconoclasm to the hearts of the unsuspecting, will be but an infinitesimal atom in the realm of the Unknown - when the flirtation with Death shall have ended!

Yours reproachfully,
THE DEVIL.

*

My Hysterical Little Mary: -
Ha!-ha!-ha!!
I am amused.
Even the Devil is sometimes amused, you know.

Your egotism and your genius (?) affect me periodically like a ridiculous incident that has happened to one. Ha!-ha!-ha!! They are constantly recurring to me in all the phases calculated to appeal to my marvelous sense of humor. Ha!-ha!-ha!!

You are only one among millions of your kind.

Thousands of other have reached the age of nineteen years, and have still retained their faculties to a much greater degree than you have. Countless scores of others have been blessed with a stronger mind, a more human heart, and a more perfect body. God's laws of existence do not apply solely to you, nor was the Devil's kingdom created alone for your enjoyment.

Out of the Nothingness of your life, you have given to the world a conglomeration of nothing - neatly expressed, I grant you - and the rebound has been NOTHING.

You have not become, as you expected, the cynosure of the world's eyes. A few brows have been lifted askance, a few eye-glasses turned in your direction; then the world will assume the even tenor of its way, and you will be left still more alone, to battle with the Nothingness which your morbid fancy has created.

The world is made up of people who eat three meals a day (if they can get them), walk a little, work a little, read a little, then lie down to sleep; who live in houses with triangular gables, who endeavor to adorn these habitations - and who find it necessary to use tooth-brushes.

There is absolutely nothing indicative in the fact that you tire of your commonplace surroundings. Dissatisfaction is one of the Devil's cleverest tricks.

The washer-woman tires of the sight of soiled linen; the patient mother tires of the prattle of babes; the daughter of fortune tires of the fawning of the world; the banker tires of columns of figures; the king tires of the duties of royalty; the overworked water-horse tires of the weight of his harness; the world tires of its burden of life; the Devil tires of association with fools - so, you see you are only ordinary, at last.

The petty, petulant, irascible nature that would rise in the majesty of genius, and rail out against six harmless, inoffensive, undesigning, unpremeditating tooth-brushes, because they deign to maintain the same position which the hand of this same genius has given them, is pitiable in the extreme.

This may, according to your feeble conception of the word, be the mark of a genius; but the world does not care, the tooth-brushes do not care, whether you are a genius or not.

If you are a genius, *be* a genius!

Do not go into the bath-room and curse half a dozen deaf, dumb, blind, inanimate tooth-brushes!

Go out; talk to the mountains; invoke the ear of the heavens; apostrophize the universe; or, what would be just as effectual, talk to yourself - but, in the Devil's name, spare the tooth-brushes!

Go forth in your loneliness and weariness and proclaim the fact that you are a genius. Lay it before the triumphal march of the sun; dispense it through the soft moonlight; attach it to the tale of some scandal; or, if you would like it more widely circulated, confide it to your best friend - but, for the love of the Devil, don't disturb the peace of the tooth-brushes.

In your most erratic moments; when the flights of your genius are most sublime, when the little, contemptible world is most contemptible to a soul that must go beyond its limits for amusement, when your marvelous genius-sense has been entertained with the music of the spheres, do not descend in wrath upon six honest tooth-brushes, that are filling their modest sphere in life - a little niche above the ledge in the bath-room.

You may hate yourself, curse God, and love the Devil - but do not profane the tooth-brushes!

Behold the tooth-brushes! "They toil not, neither do they spin; and yet I say unto you, that even Solomon, in all his glory, was not arrayed like one of these!"

Spare the tooth-brushes!

Your reprimanding
DEVIL.

*

My Own Artistic Mary: -

Today I forsook the world for a while, and crept stealthily into Sapho's study.

Now, do not allow the green-eyed monster to take possession of you, Mary, for I assure you that my motives were entirely honorable, and, furthermore, that you have a very wrong conception of Sapho.

I like to keep an eye upon what is going on in the world, and having a presentiment that you will hear more of Sapho in the future, I take this opportunity of telling you what the Devil knows about her.

She is not the seductive, devil-ordained siren, which you, in your haste, have imagined.

She is a poet - dream-eyed and beautiful.

She is young, slender, spirituelle. There is on her brow the stamp of genius, and in her midnight eyes the glow of inspiration!

She was clothed, like the woman of her dream, in a gown of purest white and softest texture, which hung in long sweeping folds from her alabaster shoulders to her white-sandaled feet! Her black hair was bound, like that of the women of olden Greece, with a fillet of silver, which encircled her brow, and seemed to shed a soft radiance about her head. She was seated at a quaint rosetta wood table, inlaid with mother-of-pearl; and she was either unaware of my presence, or else chose to ignore me entirely.

She is so conventional, so thoroughly respectable, so - damnably virtuous!

I felt very much like retreating - indeed, I did not believe I could be so abashed - but I put on a bold front, and said:

"Good morning, Sapho! How are you? I thought I would drop in and see if you were writing anything these days."

She turned her lustrous eyes full upon me, but said not a word.

I am sure she regarded me with grave suspicions, for she was immediately on her guard, and gave me no opportunity of forcing myself into her confidence. I, however, saying to myself, "nothing dared, nothing won," perched myself on the corner of her table, and endeavored to interest her in the Devil's affairs.

I called into play all my arts, all my blandishments.

I cited Mary MacLane, and painted in glowing colors the reward that would be hers, if she would only lend her pen to the Devil's cause.

She turned upon me in virtuous indignation, and would have done me bodily harm had I not been possessed of the marvelous ability of getting out of the way. I escaped her on all sides, and finally mounted the high book-case beyond the reach of her physical arms, though still within the radius of her lowering contempt.

She is a very close observer of people and things, and I decided in my own mind that she understands the Devil a little too well to be taken in by his adroitness.

She seized her pen and began to write, and forthwith I crept down from my elevation, and endeavored to assist her. I smiled when I saw that she had chosen, as her theme, Love - the theme which I delight, above all others, in perverting - and I said to myself, "I am going to have a voice in this."

Who, I should like to know, is better informed on this subject than the Devil? and who could present it more acceptably to the world?

As her restless, sensitive brain gave forth line after line of artistic symmetry and beauty, I, good Devil that I am, helped her to gather up the threads and weave them into a creation of matchless fervor and sublimity. So engrossed did she become that she did not heed my presence.

After the work was finished (or so I hoped), and she had appended the lines -

Sink their souls into a swoon
Of love unguess'd, undream'd, unknown!

- she began to scrutinize this child of her brain, to see if it were deserving of a place in the little volume which she was compiling for publication.

I sat with bated breath, fearing that the verdict would be to exclude this, the most perfect gem of her poetic sense, when she caught up her pen and added, so swiftly that I could not prompt her by so much as a single word, the sad finale - the bitter aftermath of sin!

That, Mary MacLane, is life's tragedy!

Oh, "the deep, returning ocean!" It is as cruel as death - as resistless, as overwhelming as Hell itself! The little pleasure craft, Love, is borne far inland on the crest of its mighty wave, and left stranded high above any possible tide!

There, from her desolate height, she looks down with passionate entreaty at the sea, and forever prays him to reach out his caressing arms, and fold her again to his heart!

He could not, if he would!

Later, as my rapt-eyed poetess sat reviewing the whole, meditating upon its merits and demerits, halting, as it were, between the two, I snatched it from her unsteady hand, and fled.

There was no overtaking me.

I had saved from a possible consignment to the flames, a poem of unusual beauty and passionate intensity, and I give it to you, first of all, Mary. I am sure you will appreciate it, as you are possessed of the poetic sense to a remarkable degree.

Indeed I am persuaded that you could write very creditable verses yourself.

Sapho may frown when she sees it. She may berate me for my theft. But what does the Devil care? He has been the recipient - the patient, uncomplaining recipient - of nothing but denunciation and vituperation since the world began.

Even those who profess to love me swear at me. But what does the Devil care? After I have given the poem to the world I will steal hack to her study, and, without the compunction of a child returning a stolen toy, will lay it on her table.

Poor Sapho, the Devil outwitted you this time!

He stole your poem, but he is honest enough to admit that it is not his own, but that of beautiful, dream-eyed Sapho.

*

THE GLAMOUR

'Tis a dreamy afternoon
In the languorous month of June:
A fountain, as in conscious play,
Tosses silver-beaded spray,
Casting rainbows, evanescent,
In a triple-banded crescent,
'Thwart a western window, where
Sit a man and woman fair.
'Neath the soft prismatic hues,
Like a mist of colored dews,
The woman seems transfigured there!
Purple tints are on her hair,
And in her great Egyptian eyes
Shine the lights of Paradise!
The blush of dawn is on her brow,
And on her breast the drifted snow.
Her long diaphanous gown of white
Hangs like folds of soft moonlight
From her shoulders, bare and slender
Lo! the radiant, burning splendor
Transforms the man into a god
Like Mercury, with feet flame-shod!

That strange light in his lambent eyes -
Does it come from rainbow dyes?
And that quiver in his lips,
As he kissed her finger tips,
Almost wakes her from the spell
Which o'er her wav'ring senses fell!
Ah! The look of terror dies
In her dark and slumbrous eyes,
And her head sinks on his breast
Like a bird that finds its nest.
His face bends low and lower, till
Her veins like threads of fire thrill!
On his lips, e'en now forgiven,
Seem to hang the dews of Heaven!
On his breath the roseful odor
Almost makes her bosom shudder
With a spasm of ecstasy!
A flash of lightning in his eye
Says: "My soul I'd sell for this -
This *glowing, burning, rapturous kiss!*"
His lips meet hers! Earth seems to merge
In Heaven! She dimly knows they verge
On the brink of an abyss,
In that wild, compelling kiss!
Floating on a sapphire sea,
Strewn with primrose petals, she
Knows not, cares not where or whither,
So they drift along together.
Bodies melting, souls commingling,
Brains forgetting, pulses tingling,
On they float to fields supernal,
Dreaming all this bliss eternal!
In their blood, a seething fire,
In their brains, a wild desire!
Unable to contain the measure
Of this all-consuming pleasure,
Sink their souls into a swoon
Of love unguess'd, undream'd, unknown!
*

Alas! They soon begin to waken!

Like a lily, bruised and broken,
In his arms she lies, while slow
Fades the glamour and the glow!
Wifely honor in the dust!
Violated husband's trust!
And for what? Ah, God, *what not,*
While the bliss is unforgot!

*

Slowly, slowly, back they're drifting,
While the rosy veil is lifting;
Helpless to resist the motion
Of the deep, returning ocean!

*

The sun is set; the rainbow fled,
Which o'er their forms and faces shed
An aureole of living fire.
O, the wraith of quenched desire!
Nothing, save the deadly gallows,
Casts more ghastly, ghostly shadows!
Back, at last, to life and duty;
Vanished is their dream of beauty;
And they kneel, and weep above
The grave of rashly murdered Love!

*

Yours poetically,
THE DEVIL.

*

My Mary of Moods: -
   A genius - and one hundred years ahead of your time!
   You should be able to serve the Devil's cause quite admirably. However, the Devil's work must be cleverly done, and he must make no mistakes. A further analysis of yourself might give him a clearer insight into your capabilities.
   Poor, lonely, premature Mary MacLane!
   The path of genius is solitary at best. Though strewn with tokens of the world's admiration, and illumined with the light of inspiration, the way must, nevertheless, be trod alone. The world may sit by and look at its passing, but it never enters the race.

Genius lives in an atmosphere of its own.

Why?

Because it would scorn association with the world? Because it would hate its natural surroundings? Would it build unto itself a temple in the flesh, and then despise its architecture?

It is only the mind of genius that can descend to the level of those less gifted than itself - only the eagle in its flight that can comprehend the circumscribed sphere of the meadow lark.

You look upon the world with a cold, unsympathetic eye; and because, through the very perversity of your nature, you refuse to see anything but the blots, are you a genius? Because you have taken existing conditions, and, according to the standard of your own philosophy, you have found discrepancies and inconsistences, are you a genius?

Are such sweeping assertions as, "men are idiots," and "women are inane," the deductions of genius?

Is it only fools who accommodate themselves gracefully to their sur-roundings; only fools who measure life by a standard? only fools who prefer to find good rather than evil? Is it because you hate your mother, revile the memory of your dead father, and go into hysterics at the sight of a tooth-brush, that you fancy you are a genius?

In fact, now, Mary, what have you ever done to convince the world that you are a genius?

You have "penetrated into the deep shadows?"

Ah, but you have remained there! A genius would have emerged into the effulgence of truth.

You may believe yourself to be a genius; but this hallucination will bring you little satisfaction, until the world proclaims you such.

After all, it rests with the world - the "poor, stupid world."

The epithets of denunciation which you have hurled at mankind will prove to be as preposterous as a pop-gun aimed at the moon. Or, to come down to a more likely plane, you have assimilated the petulance of a child who pouts and says unkind things of her mother, because, in the distribu-tion of apples, she did not get the largest and reddest one in the lot.

Go off into your corner and pout, little girl; but do not come forth and assert, "I am a genius!" That will never induce the little brother to give back to you the apple you coveted.

Do not deplore your fancied ill-timed appearance. An apostle of the Devil was never out of date.

Since man's incarnation, the forces of sin have been at work; and many before you have risen up and declared themselves to be the Devil's anointed.

Even the Devil is a little leery of such sweeping protestations.

I take nothing for granted, and before I can believe you are a genius you must demonstrate the fact. Your course, so far, has been such as to evoke condemnation, not only from the world - but also from the Devil as well.

A hundred years ahead of your time!

And what do you imagine the world will be a hundred years hence?

Will the stern doctrines of decency and of right have disappeared? Will the marriage ceremony - that God-ordained rite, without which the home itself were impossible - have been obliterated? Will the evil propensities of human nature then run riot? Will there be no work for the Devil to do?

Will genius enclose itself in a magnifying glass, and egotism become a cardinal virtue? Will family ties have been dissolved, and mother-love have become a legend of the past?

Will there be no counter force then to declaim against the philosophy of Mary MacLane?

There may be no tooth-brushes on the ledge in the bath-room, no "pile of stones and a barrel of lime" on the vacant lot across the street; but humanity, and the laws governing humanity, will still remain the same - in spite of all you and I can do, Mary.

There shall be "marrying and giving in marriage" even when the Lord comes.

The forecast of the world which you have risen to declare is for some future world instead, Mary.

The Devil can only laugh at your blundering, hypothetical, sin-warped logic; and smile at your self-created genius and your hell-bought egotism. He deplores the fact that you are not loved by the world, for his most successful votaries are usually those who come from the ranks of the world's anointed; and not those who are disgruntled with the world, and serve the Devil for want of a better cause.

Before you become acceptable to even the Devil, you must rid yourself of the absurdity that you are a genius. Assume any role that you are capable of sustaining, but do not call down upon your head the wrath of the Devil by exposing in such an unguarded manner the secret workings of your heart.

Take your fancied genius into custody.

Do not let the spoiled child of your bosom drag out, for the edification of strangers, the skeleton from the family closet.

Until you have learned to hide your teeth and cushion your claws, I will hesitate to entrust to you any great commission.

No one would knowingly take a rattlesnake to his bosom.

You may charm, with the necromancy of your kind, the man-devil whom you await - but you can never capture him. The poisoned fangs which you have exhibited would deter even *me*.

Consider your ways, for there is much I would have you do.

Your kind and counseling
DEVIL.

*

My Own Strenuous, Tempestuous Mary: -

Periodically, you fall "completely, madly in love with the Devil!"

Ha!-ha!-ha!

Periodically! That is a nice, convenient way of falling in love. *In*, part of the time; and *out*, the rest of the time.

Few lovers, I think, least of all the Devil, would be satisfied with such a love. Still, in your case, it is almost a necessity, Mary, because of the nature and intensity of your passion. You could not endure the boiling, seething caldron of such a love as you describe, without an occasional respite.

No one could live with "sparks of fire and ice crystals" running riot in his veins constantly; with a thousand pin-points piercing his flesh, and "every other point a point of pleasure, and every other point a point of pain!" Besides, he would surely strangle, with a stream of "milk and honey and the blossoms of the cherry" flowing down his throat continually.

It struck me that would be a good mixture for a cough syrup - milk and honey and the blossoms of the cherry. You might get a patent on it, Mary, so that you wouldn't need to write any more Portrayals.

You know what it is to love, little girl, without any doubt; but do you know what it is to be loved - and by the Devil, in the Devil's own fashion?

Perhaps I am not always the gay, debonair creature you have pictured, sitting so nonchalantly beside you in a "frail willow chair."

Of course, though, I can be all things to all men.

To you, I have "fascinating steel-grey eyes" (because you like them), "strong steel arms" (because you like them), and am enchantingly, adorably wicked!

I am bold, complacent, self-supreme!

I have the power to arouse within you a fiery passion, that shall consume you - body and soul! I can press you with my strong steel arms till you could wish that life, death, *eternity*, were measured by the limit of the Devil's arms!

Again, those same steel-grey eyes can chill the timid, shrinking heart with one look from their frigid depths. Every impulse of tenderness and sympathy they can wither with one glance from their frozen orbs; and cause the most eager to repudiate sentiments, at once the most worthy and most god-like.

It is no idle boast to say that I can crush almost any heart by my stolid indifference. The average human can buffet heat or cold, praise or condemnation, but falters beneath the sphinx-like spell of indifference. Many of my most notable victories have been won by the application of blank, bitter indifference!

What is more fatal to love than indifference? What chills the finer sentiments more surely than indifference? What congeals the fountain of affection like the cold, grey cloud of indifference? What is more effectual in retarding the work of the lowly Nazarene than indifference? Yea, He says to His very own, "I know thy works, that thou art neither cold nor hot; I would that thou wert cold or hot."

It is this noisome, withering, blood-sucking, death-laden atmosphere of indifference, which I diffuse throughout the length and breadth of the world, that reaps for me the richest harvest.

Then, on the other hand, I can melt with consuming fire the armor beneath which many a soul is lurking.

I can pierce deep!

I can tear away the veil of conventionality and expose the tender, shrinking soul to the fierce light of my eyes, and paralyze its strength by the force of my personality. I can penetrate its inmost depths and cause it to fall prostrate at my feet. I can force myself into the sanctity of its virtue; and, with the hot, hot kisses of my devilish desire, awake the passion that lies slumbering there, and make it rise to meet my own.

Yes, I can take the pure, divine love between man and woman, and work a world of evil.

Love, home, country, honor, I can plunge at once into the relentless tide of an ungoverned, chaotic passion.

I can gaze into the eyes of purity, melt the shroud in which kind nature has enwrapped it, breathe upon its senses love's sweet intoxication - until it trembles, falls, and is lost in mad delirium!

I can pour into men's veins a wild, consuming, compelling ecstasy, for the which life would be of no account, and Heaven would be dearly bought - an overwhelming flood that knows no law, no limitations, no god, but its own desire!

Yes, this is my greatest glory!

It was for this, that I entered Paradise; for this, that I have followed the course of men and women through the ages; for this, that I worm myself into the confidence of wives; and steal upon the dreams of maidens.

Is it for this, little Mary MacLane, that you implore me to come to you? For this, that you pine in loneliness and gloom - this glamour of Hell - this "red, red light" of the Devil's presence?

Is not your soul already awakened?

What devil-saint has kissed your fervid passion into life?

What forerunner has told you of the glory of Lucifer, "the son of the morning," who should follow?

What revelation is there for me to impart, since you have grasped the full realization of your awakening?

What mystic fancy could I weave, whose spell has never bound you?

What gentle murmur could I whisper, whose music has not charmed you?

What silent chord could I awaken, whose pathos never touched you?

What slumbering passion could I stir, whose power has not enthralled you?

What flowery path could I spread before you, wherein your feet have never wandered?

What rainbow could I bend above your skies, whose ribands never dazzled you?

What treasures could I lay before you, which yet remain ungathered?

What, in short, little Mary MacLane, do you want with *me*?

Your self-complacent
DEVIL.

*

My Little Genius (for I sometimes think you are such): -

"A pile of Stones and a Barrel of Lime!"

A wonderful theme for contemplation!

Well, it is something, at last, to *be* - a Pile of Stones and a Barrel of Lime; although the Devil fails to see any possibilities in either, except as they affect Mary MacLane.

A Pile of Stones and a Barrel of Lime is surely a Pile of Stones and a Barrel of Lime!

Whether they fill you with enthusiasm over their possibilities, or whether they drag you lower by the very sordidness of their individuality, they are nevertheless - a Pile of Stones and a Barrel of Lime!

Rains may come, and floods may rise; the hot winds of the desert may sweep against their responseless dimensions; summer may smile, or winter may frown at their unsightly proportions; charitable vines may weave a web of verdure around their rude exterior, and the chipmunk may find a safe retreat behind their stony portals; but they will nevertheless remain - a Pile of Stones and a Barrel of Lime!

Through man's efforts they might be lifted up into a structure of artistic beauty, and be dedicated, according to man's conception, as a temple of God; or they might be made to assume the form of the Devil's annex. In either case, they would still be - a Pile of Stones and a Barrel of Lime!

They might resound with an anthem of thanksgiving, or groan under the excesses of vice; they might harbor a home of love and happiness, or become the tenement of sin and prostitution; but they would still be - a Pile of Stones and a Barrel of Lime!

When you sit with your head pillowed upon your arm against the window-sill, and gaze with Madonna-like affectation into the space before you, the Devil regrets that the only apparition that rises up to confront you is - a Pile of Stones and a Barrel of Lime.

He can lead you through lofty flights of imagination, he can torture you with the mythical presence of the man-devil; he can pilot you to the height of your passionate desire, and can point you to the happiness which is ever in the future; but you must surely return to - a Pile of Stones and a Barrel of Lime!

The Devil himself might go to you - he might take to you the happiness that you await - but the dream would soon pass, and nothing real would remain but - a Pile of Stones and a Barrel of Lime!

The Devil might love you for "three days," he might abandon himself for that length of time to the enjoyment of your proffered passion; but, with his disappearing, would arise before you in startling vividness - a Pile of Stones and a Barrel of Lime!

He might take you in his arms, and waft you to a clime of bliss unknown, unthought, unmeasured; he might lull you into dreams that would disclose to you the Paradise of Hell; but you would surely awake to the stubborn vision of - a Pile of Stones and a Barrel of Lime!

The Devil might respond to your litany; he might deliver you from the damnable Nothingness of your life - even from yourself - but *never* from - a Pile of stones and a Barrel of Lime!

The Devil has always been the Devil.

He has made many wars and won many victories. The archives of the world are filled with his records. He has swept the principles of truth from their pedestals, and marred the most sacred handiwork of God! He has injected into the very heart of humanity the poison of his own personality, disclaimed the existence of virtue, and laughed in derision at the thought of honesty and honor. He has robbed manhood of its glory, womanhood of its crown, and prostituted at his feet the noblest work of God!

He has wrecked body, brain, and soul! But he can neither damn nor deify - a Pile of Stones and a Barrel of Lime!

He can take your wooden heart and torture it with the most exquisite pain; bruise it, break it, torment it into insensibility; but he is powerless to move - a Pile of Stones and a Barrel of Lime!

You are right, little girl; the sun moves, the stars set, the moon peeps at you for a season, and is gone; the breezes whisper a song of the sunny south, or whistle a cadence from the frozen north - then pass on; the Devil, while ever present, is always shifting his position, like the flitter in a kaleidoscope; but there ever remains in unchallenged constancy - a Pile of Stones and a Barrel of Lime!

Ha!-ha!-ha!! Hate them for their sordidness; turn from their inertia; curse the world because of them; damn them; damn everything; they will nevertheless remain, like the Sphinx, mute, immovable, impressionable - a Pile of Stones and a Barrel of Lime!

After all, since they are the only real things in life, what would you do, if there were no Pile of Stones and Barrel of Lime?

Yours, with the constancy of - a Pile of Stones and a Barrel of Lime,
THE DEVIL.

*

My Presumptuous Mary: -

And who are *you*, that you should ask the world for love?

Can it be that you, who have reviled the world: who have found your keenest enjoyment in misinterpreting the natural beauties of the world; you, to whom the poetry of sound is but a hideous jargon; you, who would make love the "by-word and the jeer" of every human tongue - have asked for its bestowal?

Can love, which is the "fulfillment of the law," find an abiding-place in a heart which contains the "germ of every crime"? Can the being, whose paramount desire is to cultivate these germs until they become a "ravaging disease," ever harbor a sentiment of love?

What right have you, who have never loved the world, to ask the world to love you?

We reap what we sow.

She who has sown hatred, contempt, selfishness, and sin, will surely reap the legitimate harvest therefrom.

"Do men gather grapes of thorns, or figs of thistles?"

What can you, who have never loved anything but an imaginary idol, know of love? How can your soul, that has always been inimical to every influence that might awaken a vibration of love, look for love in others? The fountain of your existence has been closed against the pure, crystal waters of love, and has sent forth only defilement from its own pollution.

Can the heart which has never felt a sympathetic beat, win sympathy from others? Can the hand which never offered a gracious gift of love or charity, ever hope to grasp their recompense? Can those eyes, which never saw the beauty of the world around, ever behold the blessedness of human-kindness? Can those lips which are always curled in scorn, ever melt under the rapture of a divine love? Can that soul, which has no instinct but for crime, ever receive the measure of an all-consuming, all-powerful, eternal love?

Love is not drawn into the cold, stony paths of selfishness nor courted by the revelations with which you have attempted to invite it.

The intensity which you have endeavored to construe as a capacity for love is only another way of conveying to the world your unparalleled selfishness and your unpardonable egotism.

Love is not won by a renunciation of its principles, nor held by the abandonment of that which first called it into existence.

Love seeks its own.

It lingers around the paths of those who cherish and receive it, of those whose hearts have been enriched by the overflow from their own abundance, and finds an eternal dwelling-place in those lives which have been shaped according to its own precepts.

It sometimes halts at the door of those who blindly sacrifice it on the altar builded to its own honor and glory!

Then, Love is gone; but its shadow remains - its ever haunting shadow! Over the brilliancy of song and revelry is cast the gloom of its disappearing! Upon many a scene of mirth and gladness, its mythical impress is traced. Across many a life where pleasure reigned, its tall, gaunt arm appears like the finger of Fate!

The shadow of love is more weird, more terrifying, more insupportable, more vast, than - NOTHINGNESS!

Is it only vacancy - complete vacancy - that you know, or has the gaunt spectre of love spread its lengthening outlines across the way of your young life? Is it the first appearing of love that you court, or are you seeking to coax into life the shadow of a departed dream?

Ah, Mary, believe me, nothing is so dead as a passion outlived - a vanished emotion! Nothing so impossible of resurrection as a feeling outgrown, or forgotten!

You hold out your hand to the world, as a mendicant, and beg for love - *love*! You curse the world that it gives you a stone.

Why should you? The world loves only those who love the world.

Love, and the world loves with you;
Hate, and you hate alone.

Forget yourself, your loneliness, your genius (?), your wickedness, long enough to give the world a few kind thoughts, and the world will think more kindly of you.

Curse the world, and your curses, like echoes, will come back to you!

Come; assume a virtue, if you have it not. It is necessary that you should, for the furtherance of my plans. Blind the world to the hideousness of your bare soul. Masquerade in the garb of penitence before the altar of God's infinite love, and the world will be deceived by your pretenses.

Prepare to play any part I may assign to you. Count no sacrifice too great to make on the Devil's behalf, for his kingdom is at hand; and ere long, the "red, red light" of his appearing shall burst forth like a meteor upon the dull grey dawn of your young womanhood!

Yours reprovingly,
THE DEVIL.

*

My Dear Supercilious Mary: -

The Devil had a vision!

Even the Devil has visions, at times.

In some vague, indefinable way, you, Mary, were connected with this vision.

"A thing oval and crisp and good and green" appeared before me.

"A wonderful olive!" I said; "I will take it to Mary."

But no; it was not an olive tree that stood out in clear relief against the background of a California sky, and extended its fruit-laden boughs to the warm Pacific breeze; but a luxuriant vine that wound itself in rank profusion through the furrows of a cotton field.

Gradually the scene was changed; I saw a huge, lazy, gluttonous hog crush between her vise-like tusks the thing that had appeared "oval and crisp and good and green."

It was a watermelon!

I saw the look of hoggish satisfaction that crept into her hoggish eyes, as she fastened her great jaws around the fresh, crisp rind. I watched, with trepidation, the molars close upon their prey; and saw the red, juicy pulp of the melon, as it glided, to her hoggish delight, over her gustatory nerves, then disappeared into the cavernous depths of her hoggish paunch.

The vision was not sufficiently clear for me to watch the course of the melon further; but I had reason to suppose, from the greediness with which she repeated the act, that she packed it securely away somewhere, and was very much pleased with the disposal.

The vision continued.

I saw again the mighty jawbone swing open on its hinges, and another huge gulp of the melon appropriated for the entertainment of her hoggish palate and the delight of her hoggish stomach, that is in a state of constant protest, because of nature's abhorrence of a vacuum.

I saw a mighty muscular exhibition of the throat, and knew that that portion of the melon had followed the other down the course of the esophagus, and had reached its destination in the inland sea that lies at the foot of this important canal.

While I was speculating upon the nature, dimensions, etc., of this feature of hog anatomy, my attention was again directed to the business end of the hog, as she continued to lay in, with evident satisfaction to her hoggish appetite, the remainder of the melon.

The vision faded; but not before I had seen the last piece of rind disappear in the same manner as the first, and heard her hoggish grunt of satisfaction, as she went back to her wallow.

The Devil is convinced of one fact, Mary; and that is, that though you may have "acquired the art of eating an olive," the hog has also acquired the art of eating a watermelon!

Your very epicurean
DEVIL.

*

My Bold, Arrant Mary: -

Yours, little MacLane, is not the only heart that feels the weight of weariness.

Even I get weary sometimes, and like to withdraw to the mountain height for meditation. The divers necessities of my position press heavily upon me, and I like to cease for a season from even the contemplation of my own victory.

I am surfeited with the dumb, dog-like devotion of the populace. The coarse, vulgar demonstrations of the common herd, at times, grate sharply upon my keen sensibilities.

I am bored.

I am disgusted with the low, groveling throng that serves me only through the lusts of the flesh. I have a sense of the beautiful, the aesthetic, the sublime, the romantic, which shrinks from common, sordid vice.

Of course, I must smile when it confronts me. I must approve all demonstrations of loyalty; but often it is with regret that the tendency of sin is toward such a low, vulgar, vicious level.

What glory can the Devil find in the loyalty of a subject who has not the instinct to serve a higher master? What pride can he feel in the destruction of those whose souls are dead to every counter impulse? Can the life which was shaped by only the vilest influences, add much brilliancy to the Devil's kingdom?

I am weary; I am disgusted; more than this, I am annoyed.

The complete abandon of these creatures brings my kingdom into disrepute.

Who, by beholding the drunkard in the gutter, will follow his footsteps? Who, by witnessing the ravings of the self-convicted criminal, will easily be drawn into the mesh of crime? When did the harlot, in her abandoned state, ever tempt womanhood from the path of virtue and honor?

To induce others to follow in her footsteps, she must be clothed in the silken weave of foreign looms and the hand-wrought laces of many lands. She must wear the rose on her cheek, the dew on her lip, and the jasmine odor on her breath. Her voice must be soft as a purling stream, her eyes like stars of Arcady, and her breasts like cones of snow, tipped, each, with a carnation petal.

She must breathe the incense of violets; repose on couches of broidered velvet, canopied with golden tissue; and bathe her beautiful body in the costly distillation of roses!

She must be studded with jewels, as the Milky Way is with stars. Diamonds, that burn with a pure white light like the sacred fire in the temple of Vesta; emeralds, whose shimmering sheen is like glints of sunlight on the sea-wave; sapphires, crystallized fragments of Italia's skies; rubies, those roseate gems, baptized by the gods in the sunrise; and pearls, beautiful emblems of a soul without sin - all, all must lend their grace to her enchantment!

Ah, thus, she is a rare exotic - a red, red rose of voluptuousness!

With the spell in her eyes, and the syren-song in her voice, she leads men on to madness, and women - down into the very jaws of Hell!

Without her, I should have been vanquished long ago, and my kingdom portioned out to the righteous. She is my best bower, and when I play her for a soul, who dares say that soul is not mine?

But - rob her of her glory; in the place of the perfume on her breath, put the vile stench of liquor; where the rose-glow shone on her cheek, set the shameless seal of debauchery; strip off her gorgeous raiment, and clothe her in the rags of pollution; instead of the voluptuous couch hung with tissue of gold, give her a pallet of straw for a bed; in the place of the gay birds-of-paradise which circled in her wake, send her, for companions, the bloated vultures of dissipation - and she becomes the greatest stumbling-block in my path.

Yes, I am distressed at the flagrant, atrocious manner in which the consequences of evil are stamped upon the world.

Oh, that it could always wear the shining aspect of its author - who has been likened unto an "angel of light!"

If I should appear in all the hideousness of my natural self, how many would embrace me? If I should dangle before their eyes the recompense of my service, how many would follow me, do you think?

It is when they drop the mantle of dissemblance, and the world is permitted to see them in all the blackness of sin, that my wretched, vagabond subjects cease to be an honor to me.

I tire, I weary of them!

Constant association with their weakness, their helplessness, their groveling condition, only wakens for them a greater contempt.

I can tell you all these things with impunity, Mary, because you have already agreed to my conditions. For the Happiness which I shall bring you - be it only for an hour - you have sworn to give up: "Fame, and Money, and Power, and Virtue, and Honor, and Righteousness, and Truth, and Logic, and Philosophy, and Genius" - the while you will say:

"What a little, little price to pay for dear Happiness!"

I take me to the everlasting mountains, where from the full height and majesty of my position, I can contemplate the world around me.

Grand, magnificent world! whose primeval glory is flecked and marred by my invisible presence! From the most exalted height to the lowest depth of human existence, I have entered.

Yea, I have forced myself into the very presence of the Maker, and have tempted the King of Righteousness!

I have entered the "holy of holies," and have sipped the Vestal dews from the budding rose of womanhood. I have found my way into the privacy of queens, and have robbed them of the glory of their crown. I have wielded the sceptre of thrones, and have poured confusion into the hearts of the world's greatest leaders. I have corrupted the lives of those ordained to the service of God, and have routed their followers in mad disorder.

Ah, there is glory in this!

To thwart the purposes of God through the means of His anointed; to pervert the truth in the minds of those who seek after it; to lure the conscientious into the ways of sin; to cause the upright to stumble; to steal the virtue of those who realize its worth; to break down the faith of those who live only in the light of its beneficence: - ah, these are tributes to my infinite power!

There is glory - there is recompense to this!

Poor deluded world! you are deceived by my brass and tinsel, and sell your soul for a mess of pottage!

Yet, there are conquests still unachieved.

There are many humble hearts in which the troth burns brightly, many lives which have been guided around my pitfalls, many souls that have become partakers of the life eternal.

These I must tempt.

I shall revile the promises by which they are upheld. I shall sap the power and energy of their leaders, and strengthen the arm of luxury and lust. I shall gild afresh the aureole of wealth, and harden the hearts of the oppressors. I shall make the path of sin yet more alluring, and shall cause it to cross and re-cross the way of righteousness, until the two are lost in a labyrinth of confusion!

Yea, there are delicate tasks for me to perform. To pour the poison of jealousy into a happy home; to wean the husband from the fire-side, and lure the wife into the ways of dishonor; to sow the seeds of enmity and doubt in the hearts of their offspring: and to make the memory of their home a travesty on all that is good and pure.

Yes, this is the Devil's work, and it must be cleverly done.

Before I enlist your aid, little Mary MacLane, I must assure myself that you are in all respects fitted to perform the work required of you.

I can only say to you at present, "Wait." I must move with deliberation, and, in the work which lies before me, I must make no mistakes in selecting my deputies. So, I repeat to you, "Wait."

My coming may be delayed - but I shall surely come!

Yours in deliberation,
THE DEVIL.

*

My Little Caricaturist: -

In my dutiful round among the smart set, the literary set, the card set, the dancing set, and every other set (I omit none), I meet with varied experiences. Some are ludicrous, some are even pathetic.

Today I straggled in where a coterie of heavy-cheeked, heavy-headed, would-be champions of Kipling were holding forth. They professed an immoderate liking for his writings, especially his mechanical verse.

I will confess to you, Mary (but do not tell anybody), that I find about as much real pleasure in reading Kipling as a frog would find at a beauty show. However, when I go to the Kipling Club I pretend a superlative fondness for his grotesque English and his quaint metaphors.

Tonight a curious-looking object (of doubtful gender) in male attire, arose and delivered in stirring tragedy, that gem of Kipling's verse - "The Vampire."

I sat speechless!

The eyes of this creature rolled and walled as though their movements were regulated by some automatic attachment; his arms circumvolved frantically, like those of a wind-mill in a veritable gale; and his countenance underwent that series of contortions incidental to an overdose of Compound Cathartic Pills.

On inquiry, I found that this nondescript had a bad case of "stageitis," which was liable to result fatally at any moment - fatally to the public.

However, his distractingly realistic demonstration of the tragedy embodied in the poem set me to thinking - and when I begin thinking, Mary, sooner or later my thoughts revert to you.

The mechanical jingle in the verse had made me dizzy, like much turning in a waltz; so that when the recitation came to a close my thoughts refused to stop. They kept right on, in spite of me:

*

A woman there was, and she made her prayer
(As anyone might do),
To the Devil, the Devil himself, debonair -
To the *Devil*, I say, do you hear?
To the red, red *Devil in Hell*, I swear -
(A pity, but nevertheless true!)

*

Oh! the wail that she wold, and the prayer that she prayed!
(The Devil himself was amazed.)
'Twas a plea from the dumb, wooden heart of a maid -
A volume of protest, wickedly laid
In the path of the Devil - to tempt him, by gad! -
(But the Devil was awfully pleased.)

*

A woman there was, and she told her tale
(As you or I might do),
Of a world-full of Nothing, a bargain-day sale
Of herself to the Devil (egad! what a deal!)

And her fruitless endeavor to capture a male
(A deed she would probably rue).
*

Oh, the moans and the groans - and that desolate cry -
'Twould melt e'en the Devil to tears!
(Ha!-ha!-ha! - and wouldn't a Devil in tears be a guy?)
That a woman young and alone must sigh
On the breast of a rock, when the Devil is nigh,
Is a pitiful state of affairs!
*

A woman there was who was weary of life
(As you or I might be),
The stupid old world with its bandying strife,
Its conventional codes, as absurd as they're rife.
By Jove she would be the Devil's own wife!
(A fortunate (?) Devil he!)
*

"Come up, O Devil, to a maiden fair,
Come up from the depths of Hell,"
She cried; "and hearken thee to the prayer
Of 'a rag and a bone and a hank o' hair,'
Wailing her wail of wild despair,
Which nothing on earth can quell!
*

"A *man* I want, and a man I must have -
One steeped in wickedness -
In fact, O Devil, 'tis *thee* I crave!
Come to my arms, and I'll be thy slave;
For none, none, I swear, but thyself can save
My soul from its NOTHINGNESS!"
*

The world was not moved by the things that she said
(A genius; too, tra-la-la-);
But the Devil in Hell - the Devil red, red -
Heard the prayer that she prayed, and he wilfully staid
Till he captured the heart of this mischievous maid
(A devilish trick-ha!-ha!-ha!!).
*

Your paradoxical
DEVIL.

*

My Erratic, Intrepid Mary: -

Again, I thank you, little MacLane, for what you have done, and for what you continue to do in my behalf. Indeed, I begin to realize that there is much already for which I should feel grateful to you.

At one time, I am eminently pleased with you; but again, I am disappointed. I no sooner look with favor upon your cunning and your craft, than I am disconcerted by your inconsistencies.

In one hand, you play your cards cleverly enough, but in the next, you trump the Devil's ace.

Be careful, little girl; make no rash plays, and thus expose your hand to the conjecture of those who are ever on the defensive.

You have one magnificent hand, and you must play it worthily.

It is that winning, seductive, soul-stupefying theory that there is no evil, except in the minds of those who conceive it. Proclaim this to the world; press it home to the hearts of those who have dared to think for themselves.

It savors of the *new*, the *progressive*, the *occult*. It carries with it a suggestion of "*ism*" and "*ology*" that is quite pedantic.

Many will embrace it, because it asserts their prerogative to individuality; and claims to endow them with mentality sufficient to control the great forces of good and evil. It reduces the Devil and his angels to a condition of mysticism, and its votaries imagine that it gives the feeble, whimsical, inconsistent mind of man absolute dominion over the Devil.

According to this theory there is an impersonal, stultifying, compelling influence, which, when the Creator was setting in motion the vast machinery of the universe, somehow or other got loose and has ever since been flying at random, disturbing the equilibrium of the world.

Teach the people, Mary, that this influence is an evil, and a corrupter of good morals *only* when they choose to consider it such - that nothing, not even that which emanates directly from the Devil himself, is evil *of itself.*

When this idea becomes firmly established, it will then be an easy matter to persuade the world that there is no evil whatever. The theory will prove itself; for no individual will acknowledge to himself, or to the world, that *he is evil.*

Do not reason with those who might protest against this indiscriminate disposal of all that is inimical to the cause of righteousness.

Ridicule their theories.

There is no argument you can employ; so meet them with the weapon that few can resist - ridicule.

The world is easily deceived; and when you present to it a lie that it would like to believe, it accepts it without question. Many a spectre of vice, however hideous, but for the barrier of conventionality would be received as a welcome guest.

Delude the world into believing that there is no evil in anything that it earnestly covets; because, prejudiced in its own favor, it sees no evil in the object of its desire. Seeing none, emphasizes the fact that there can possibly be none.

Having gone thus far, it is only a step to the Devil's kingdom.

Poor deluded world! and you, Mary MacLane, its would-be leader!

Will the prick of the thorn be less acute because you trod upon it unawares? Will the poison of the adder be less deadly because you did not descry the reptile as it lay half buried in the sand? Was the fury of Mount Pelee ameliorated in the least because its unfortunate victims did not foresee their impending danger?

Will the damnation of a wasted, sin-cursed life be less real because one did not believe its tendencies were evil?

How much more immutable and inexorable, then, are the laws of eternal right and wrong!

The fact that some poor, egotistical, self-conceited genius (?) has risen up and declared that he was honest in believing that his course was right, will not make the Devil's victory any less complete.

Eve was honest in believing my promises that her eyes should be opened, and that she should be as a god; but nevertheless she was driven out into darkness, and "there was placed at the east of the garden of Eden Cherubims, and a flaming sword which turned every way, to keep the way of the tree of life."

We might coax the nightingale to sing at noonday; but the hour would still be noon. Through artifice we might force the lily to bloom at Christmastide; but it would still be bleak December.

The Devil assumes many disguises; the world looks on and applauds the masquerade; but he is nevertheless the same shrewd, cunning, crafty, snaky, subtle, insidious Devil!

Though transformed into an angel of light, or steeped in the crimson of Hell; though enshrined as a deity of love, or scorned as a demon of hate; though worshiped as the Prince of the earth, or abhorred as a spirit of darkness, the Devil is the Devil still!

He not only obliterates the ravages of his march, but he conceals his own identity so cleverly that there are many who go forth and proclaim to the world:

"Fear not; there is no evil. Evil is only a phantom that lurks in the minds of the superstitious. So-called sin is no longer the tyrant that we were taught to believe. Everything is good; evil exists only in a crude, out-of-date, devil-haunted mind."

Those who thus deceive themselves build best of all, to the honor and glory of the Devil!

You, little Mary MacLane, have served him admirably, thus far; but you are equipped sufficiently well to accomplish for him still more wonderful results.

You have a hand which only the artful, the cunning, the crafty, can play. Turn it over to the drunken sot, or to the sin-cursed object of the world's disdain, and the trick would be lost.

You are young, winning, delightful.

The world could never associate your freshness, your charming youth, your maidenhood, with deeds of sin and wrong-doing.

Lips like yours could easily persuade the world that there is no evil. The look of assumed innocence which your clear eyes send forth, compels the world to acknowledge that if such is evil, evil cannot be so very bad.

Your pen, which has sent a ripple of eloquence from ocean to ocean, can build to the Devil a "monument more durable than brass, and more conspicuous than pyramids."

Your astute and confident
DEVIL.

*

Brimstone Chamber, Hell, 1903.

My Love-Awakened Little Girl: -

The Devil sent you a dream last night - you of nineteen years and all alone!

Does it linger with you in all the reality of an actual presence, or does it haunt you like a strain from which all melody has departed?

I made it appear as though the world had dissolved into a rosy mist, and all the black, ugly sordidness of life had melted into an infinity of perfect appointment. The air was laden with the perfume of Hesperides, and through this atmosphere of languorous delight was wafted the ripple from distant chimes.

The face of nature was blended into perfect harmony with the roseate dream that held you, and over all was cast that strange, sweet spell of infinite delight - that rare, unconscious state that seemed to bind the universe in the one word, *love* - and lay it at your feet.

The lilies murmured it to you from their waxen trumpets; the roses kissed it to you from their fragrant lips; the violets lisped it to you from their modest beds; and the humming-bird chanted it to you as he sucked the dews from flower to flower. The dove caught up the strain as she wove her nest in the boughs above you, while the breezes whispered to you the same tale of ceaseless love.

I touched your spirit and awakened your senses to a realization of your surroundings. You drank in the beauty, the harmony, the love-glory of the scene. You reveled in the contemplation of this Elysium, and fancied for a while that even you had a part in this life of love.

Again, I touched you, and your soul was roused from its sleep of peace, and you became a spectator at the feast of love. Your trembling heart was awakened, but there was for it no counterpart - no kindred soul to lead you to the fountain of love.

The sweet, clear tones of the mocking-bird, as it warbled forth its own delight, brought no message to you; it was a love-ballad to its mate. The hawthorn blossoms, with their languorous perfume, only filled your soul with a deeper longing for the joy of love.

I watched you as you contemplated this scene of nature's harmony. I saw the infinite pathos couched in your dreamy eyes, and read, in their mute supplication, the pleading of a hungry heart. I saw your arms outstretched, and heard your piteous, passionate cry:

"O, for one human heart to love me!"

Instantly, like the good Devil that I am, I appeared before you. I came in the form of a fair Adonis, in answer to that hopeless human cry.

I saw your slender figure shrink into an attitude of maidenly timidity. I watched the look of longing fade into one of childlike innocence, and I read the question that trembled on your lips before the words were framed:

"Who are you? Why are you here?"

"Who am I? One for whom you long. Why am I here? To love you!"

"To love me!" you said; and your halting tones seemed less the reverberation of a yearning soul than the awakening of a child of nature.

"To love me!" you repeated. "Will you love me?"

"*Will* I love you! *May* I love you?"

"I have been so lonely! The very beauty of my surroundings makes me afraid. The love that is everywhere seems to mock me like the irony of fate! Oh! I have been so lonely, so lonely!"

"Lonely, when you are nature's queen? When the pearly tints of space are but the setting of a picture of rarest beauty - yourself? When the perfectness of your surroundings is only the background to your own perfection? When the universality of love with which you are surrounded is but the diffused essence of the love which I bring you? When the song of the nightingale is but the outpouring of your own full heart? May I love you? You were made to be loved."

"Loved? I have never been loved."

"Until now," I said, as I drew nearer, and stooped to take your hand and press it to my lips. I saw the blush of maiden fear mount to your cheek. I watched the downcast eyes, as they were slowly lifted to my own; and I met them with such tenderness, that the look of wild, uncertain terror faded from their depths. I held their gaze in the coils of my fascination, and stretched out my arms to you. You came, like one in a trance, and I folded you to my heart - you of nineteen years and all alone!

Ah! the witchery of the Devil!

I saw a strange light leap into your eyes, and the hot waves of passion mantle your cheeks. I felt the tremor that passed through your form, and chained it to your lips with one long, compelling kiss. A moment more - and my triumph was complete!

"This, this is love!" I said.

*

There was no awakening of your faculties. Your senses slept, and conscience never knew that you had been led to my trysting place.

You dreamed that the Devil loved you!

Cherish the dream, little girl; for the awakening, ah, the awakening - but you know!

With "hot burning kisses,"
Your adorable
DEVIL.

*

My Too Garrulous and Vociferous Mary: -

Labor Day in Chicago!

What a world of meaning those few words convey!

As I stood on the curb-stone watching the procession in which thousands took their places in the ranks of those who toil, I was appalled at the magnitude and the comprehensiveness of their efforts along the lines of unification.

O, the majesty, the strength, the latent energy which that line of march represented!

The thought occurred to me that perhaps I had been a little derelict in my duty toward the world and myself by not affiliating openly and avowedly with the unions. There was a spirit of brotherhood and good fellowship which prevailed among those sons of toil, that was even touching in its simplicity. But what union would receive the Devil in his own guise?

It might not be a bad idea to start a union of my own. I could doubtless soon secure a large membership, but - horror of horrors! what if, during my most profitable season, a strike should be ordered! And wouldn't this old world be a stale, lonesome, churchyardy place with the Devil and his agents on a strike! Such a situation is too awful to contemplate, and rather than look into the future for such a possibility, I shall turn and look backward into the past.

That is mine. The past into which many gaze mournfully and remorsefully, I look with satisfaction and contentment.

Somehow tonight the memory of Cripple Creek, and all that has transpired there rises up before me, and through the glamour of retrospection, I recall particularly the last Fourth of July celebration which I spent there. I was somewhat in the dumps at the time, and needed to be aroused to keener action, so I sought out Cripple Creek - the Queen City of the Mountains, that nestles in a quaint, irregular basin at the foot of verdant hills.

Your observation of a similar occasion in Butte, makes my own experience appear apropos, for nothing that ever was in Butte has outstripped Cripple Creek.

The terrible upheavals of the Volcanic Age, which lined and relined those mountains with veins of sylvanite that have poured their fabulous stream of gold into the world's coffers, left, at a height of almost two miles, a gentle depression, and sheltered it with hills.

There, Cripple Creek is built.

Those hills - in winter, capped with snow; in summer, crowned with flowers - are dotted with numerous shaft-houses that have astonished the world with their output; while just beyond the chain, venerable Pike's Peak, hoary with age, rises like a holy sentinel!

On the other side, a solitary peak, more stately, more majestic than its neighbors, tells a tale of departed glory. An extinct crater marks the spot upon its dome from which the fiery flood of earth's impent forces once issued; and doubtless poured its lava, with the fury of an avenging spirit, upon a defenseless world.

At the foot of this mountain patriarch is the last resting-place of Cripple Creek's wealth-seekers - the City of the Dead!

There is a solemnity, an awful pathos, that rests like a benediction upon this home of eternal silence!

Feeling particularly devilish, I went there.

It is not a place where tall, gleaming monuments point toward Heaven like holy spires; where roses - perfect roses, all but their mystic fragrance - bloom in granite stone; where marble hands are clasped - never, never to unclasp; where columns, rudely broken, tell their tale of sudden death; where carved angels never forsake their vigils, because their wings are fettered in cruel stone!

It is a dreary, solitary spot, where new-made mounds succeed each other like ripples on a lake; where rude stones - instead of hovering angels - keep the solemn watches of the night; where rough, unlettered boards tell the sequel to the story of the bag of gold at the end of the ever receding rainbow! It is a lone, forsaken spot, that even Nature seems to shun; and, as if to obliterate the marks of its desolation, she covers it with a mantle of snow, long before the busy city of mines is wrapped in its wintry shroud.

Many a hope and many a dream lie buried at the foot of Mount Pisgah!

Many a soul, weary of disappointment, has sought rest within the depths of these rock-strewn mounds.

Some have found it; while the great majority have only passed over into the reality of Hell!

Most of these graves the Devil has dug; and many are the stones he has raised to mark the spot of his final victory!

Mount Pisgah cemetery is a place that mankind shuns; but I like to go there and contemplate the dire evidences of my power. The tales of blighted hopes, blasted lives, and damned souls, that are told upon this page of the annals of the dead, constitute to me a theme of great rejoicing.

In the midnight watches, I sometimes steal away from the din of revelry, and wend my way to this last resting-place of the departed. I look beyond the mound of rock and earth - deep, deep into the grave; beyond the little pile of mouldering bones - into the eternity of gloom that yawns beneath!

I look into the bottomless pit of Hell, and I say - "It is well!"

I then draw the curtain, and with renewed vigor and strengthened purpose, I return to my earthly labors.

The Fourth in Cripple Creek usually yields a rich harvest.

It is a riotous demonstration that does not savor in the least of patriotism. There is a preconcerted action on the part of the city and the city officials to advertise a "grand celebration," in the hope of securing a little monetary bounty, to supply their depleted coffers.

The crowd is thus enticed within its borders, and there is a mighty clamor, a heterogeneous hurrah for whatever is uppermost in the minds of the participants.

There is a feeble cheer for the reading of the Constitution; for, even in

Cripple Creek, whose streets, on the occasion, become a seething, boisterous mass of humanity, representing every nationality of what is called the "civilized world," there are those who honor the day for what it commemorates, and renew their vows to their country and their flag.

Simultaneously - in darky lingo - there is a loud hurrah for Abraham Lincoln; for the descendants of Ham associate the author of the Emancipation Proclamation with the Fourth of July, as with every other legal holiday the calendar of the country affords.

Then there is the majestic, weather-beaten veteran of the Confederacy, whose annals are - that he "fought with Lee;" and could the secret promptings of his heart burst forth, his voice would be raised in one grand cheer for Jeff Davis and the Lost Cause!

There is the empty-headed, empty-hearted, empty-handed Englishman, who surveys this conglomeration of humanity through his monocle much as though he were viewing an open-air burlesque on Henry VIII.

There are hordes of Erin's lusty sons, who would shout, if they dared, for Saint Patrick and the land of the Shamrock.

Then, there is the dusky son of Italy, who sees, in an occasion of this kind, an opportunity to advance the price of peanuts and bananas.

The cowboy is here in all his glory - chaps, boots, spurs, sombrero, quirt, lariat, and all - and concedes to himself the honor of entertaining the crowd with his brutal exhibitions of horsemanship.

The farmer from the little ranch down in the hollow, has come and brought the family. In an unbroken line, which measures the width of the sidewalk, they saunter up one side of the street and down the other, until the tempting displays in the store windows have robbed him of much of his hard-earned coin.

The miner is here with a day off and his best girl; and, as he puffs into her face cigar smoke and whiskey fumes, one does not wonder that the life of the miner's wife is not strewn with roses.

Through all this surging mass of humanity, pressing from one street into another, rushing almost in a stampede to a corner where a brass band holds forth, then crowding back to witness a feeble demonstration of a hose-cart race, and again surging in pandemonium to a spot where it has been announced that a stuffed rabbit, strung on a wire, will be pursued by two greyhounds - through all this the Devil goes, too.

In the forenoon there is always a pitiable attempt at a parade, the most important feature of which is the personal exhibition of the mounted police, who, "clothed in a little brief authority," are more important in their own estimation than the Devil himself!

There are those among the vast throng of on-lookers who behold this pageant with an intensity that is almost tragic, and who regard the regalia of the various secret orders as the very acme of perfection in the art of adornment.

Through this motley crowd, at once in the company of thieves and pick-pockets, and again, arm in arm with the Mayor of the city, the Devil makes his way.

He sometimes lingers with the little band of city and county officials, as they celebrate according to the license of their jurisdiction, but the Devil is no respecter of persons; and while, for many reasons, he would like to court those in authority, he never does it to the detriment of his cause among the masses.

I loiter through the drinking saloons, where men would barter their souls for a "cock-tail" or a "whiskey straight." I act as host to all who enter, but drink with none.

The Devil knows his own game!

From thence I join a group of girls and boys, who are indulging in all sorts of familiarity, which this venerable occasion seems to license. I follow them to the soda fountain, and name the drink, which, in many instances, is the stepping-stone to a life of bondage in my service.

I come out and join a group of Irish house-wives - or any other nationality, as the case may be - whose most flattering testimonials of respectability are the numerous offspring that dignify each with the cognomen, "maw;" and I hear them traduce the neighbor who lives across the alley, because she takes no part in their back-yard socials, but follows the even tenor of her way, unmindful of the fact that she is the object of neighborhood gossip.

I wend my way from group to group, ever mindful of the fact that the nation's birthday is the Devil's work-day.

I pass none by.

From the weather-beaten, wizened street peddler, who calls out the price of peanuts, popcorn, and lemonade, to the society queen, who saunters along with the air of one who is being observed, I pass with equal deference.

It is at evening, when the curtain of night is drawn, that my hitherto restricted pastime becomes an undeniable revel. I follow the aimless, thoughtless throng, as it forces its way up one side of the street and down the other.

I enter into the spirit of the occasion which licenses the throwing of confetti, the blowing of horns, the manipulation of every contrivance that will give forth sound, the significant use of carnival canes, the display of fireworks - in short, the general abandon that humanity has assumed.

The odor of whiskey-laden breath is lost in an atmosphere of powder smoke. Profane and indecent language, with which the air is rife, is unheard above the din and noise of general confusion.

Everything goes.

The Devil is turned loose.

I don my black domino, and go to the masquerade; and there, with a queen among women, I lead the grand march - to Hell!

Hundreds fall in, and erelong the Devil's march gives way to the Devil's waltz. I fold this beautiful woman to my bosom as only the Devil can, and lead her to the shrine from which is to arise the incense of her sacrificed womanhood!

I dance with the "peasant maid," the "Spanish gypsy," the statuesque Greek girl, and countless scores of others. Some, I flatter; some, I beguile; some, I dare; many, I conquer.

From the masquerade, I go to the scenes of those "fascinating, glittering bad things," which seem to possess such an enchantment for you.

Ah, this is the "red, red line of sky," that you see in the distance, Mary - the line that is dyed red with *blood*!

Many women, in spite of all my artfulness, will not be induced to even look upon it. I say to them:

"Behold! It is grand! It is magnificent! The sun is setting; and from out his golden bosom seem to burst a million flaming spears! Clouds of purple and gold are chasing each other like chariots across the breadth of sky, marked by the 'red, red line of light!'"

But no; they will not even look.

You do not believe this, Mary; but it is true, nevertheless.

This is something of the manner in which the nation's birthday is celebrated in Cripple Creek.

Ye sons of liberty, how your bones must quake at the sad way in which the day that you set aside to be observed with fitting honor, has been prostituted!

What is the meaning of the Fourth of July as it is observed today?

What was the meaning intended?

The Devil does not care. It is a fruitful day on his calendar!

Yours with exultation,
THE DEVIL.

*

My Petulant Little Mary: -

"Stupid old world!" do you say?

Ah, let me tell you something of this world, my child.

It is a fine old world, and if you were a real genius, you would perceive it. Its adjustments are perfect.

There is the springtime, when nature unfolds her verdure at the kiss of the warm south wind; when the robins nest, and the dove coos lovingly to its mate; when the crystal mountain streams burst forth from their prison of snow, and the voices of nature unite in proclaiming the glad seed-time.

The crimson-throated scorpion plays again along the ground and fences; the inconstant chameleon glides in opalescent beauty from rock to tree; while the mottled serpent, the impersonation of myself, creeps from its winter home.

Later, is the harvest time; when the great reaper of nature garners in the winter's store.

Nothing is overlooked.

The hand that fashioned the things of earth was mindful of even the atoms.

In the marvelous plan of nature, there are no dolts and sluggards - no blots to mar the beauty of a perfect whole.

All is harmony; and - "only man is vile."

Yes; proud, vain, foolish creature that man is, he has made this realm - once a stranger to the presence of evil - the Devil's play-ground.

Bright, glorious, wonderful world!

Yours contentedly,
THE DEVIL.

*

My Own Unfathomable Mary: -

Let me confide to you a secret, little girl: your Devil must surely be a hero.

Today I entered that "sanctum sanctorum," the Woman's Club.

I had been told that in all probability Mary MacLane would be discussed, so I went.

It proved to be a particularly fortunate appointment of fate that took me there, for much, aside from what was said about your wonderful self, transpired in which I am interested.

How did I enter?

I donned a shirt waist and a short skirt, assumed an intellectual air, and affected an attitude of supreme importance. I drew down the corners of my mouth, adjusted my eye-glasses, and scanned the whole gathering with the scrutiny of one looking for a wolf in sheep's clothing.

I displayed a work on parliamentary ruling, also a suspicious looking little wallet, which I contrived to make it appear as if it contained papers of importance.

I was thin-cheeked, and wore a cadaverous look that suggested patient, faithful work along the lines essayed by woman, and confirmed the suspicion that I had "mothered" many clubs.

I sat down on the lower side of my thin hips, adjusted my shoulder-blades to the back of my chair, and my sharp knees to accommodate the suspicious-looking wallet, and surrounded myself with the halo of a patriarch.

Good Devil that I am, I was practically unobserved!

Presently the meeting was called to order by a "symphony" in black and green, whose head rose from her shoulders at a forward angle of fifty degrees or less, and whose belt line was elevated in front (the pity of it!) to afford room for the disproportionate paunch, that years of ignorant, slothful attitudes had created.

The texture and style of her gown were sadly incompatible with the figure which it clothed. The stamp of commonality will show through the most gorgeous apparel; while the untaught, uncultured mind can never be masked by the accessories to the modern toilet table.

The Devil chuckled to himself as he surveyed the crowd.

How was "*it*" (the Chairman) held in the estimation of those who faced "it" (with a capital I)? This, the Devil sought to discover. The faces of some lighted up with enthusiasm, probably because "it" evinced a preference in presenting the left profile, which bore the unmistakable stamp of the female Judas, and displayed to a full advantage the real ostrich feather which her milliner had arranged quite fetchingly on that side of her head-gear.

Others seemed to wear a look of admiration, but whether it was inspired by the scintillation of the diamond sunburst that glittered upon the breast of "*it*," or whether it arose from the remembrance of the kindness of fate - a fate that had lifted "*it*" from obscurity in a little Oklahoma town, to the Presidency of the Woman's Club - the Devil could not decide.

Others wore the same stereotyped smile and pose of affectation, which had been studiously cultivated in the school of "society," and which is assumed in public, whether the occasion be an afternoon tea or a memorial service.

Still others were wrapped in an expression, at once tense and hard, that betrayed the effort being put forth to sustain the role of intellectuality and strong-mindedness. They *scorned* to observe the length of the train that spread out to the rear of "*it*."

There was a whole phalanx of those who, doubtless, according to the law of philosophy governing the attraction of likes, were as stolid and as expressionless as a piece of masonry. Just why they were there, the Devil never quite understood; but they were there in goodly numbers.

Then there was a distractingly large number - the Devil was surprised - who were there solely because the rumor had gained circulation that refreshments were to be served. They dutifully sat through the performance (Heaven help them!) sustained by the hope that the hour for the exercise of their particular talent would come after a while.

There was a final sprinkling of open, honest faces, which clearly told that they were there for mutual help and benefit.

The Devil trembled at the thought of what Mary MacLane might receive at the hands of this assemblage.

Presently, with an imperious rap of the gavel, order was called out of chaos, and the various countenances assumed intensified expressions.

With something after the order of a travesty on the Goddess Of Liberty enlightening the world, our female personification of "it" arose to deliver a salutation to her flock; and with the Ego, which was plainly uppermost in her mind, as well as cunningly woven into her remarks, the Devil at first thought that she had been reading Mary MacLane.

There was a crafty little smile, and a pensive droop of the eyelids, that were quite fetching, and, which I noted with a view of reproducing on similar occasions.

With another imperious gesture, more indicative of the mistress of a Kansas farm than of the Presiding officer of any organization of women, the wonderful machinery of the Woman's Club was in motion.

The Devil sat there unmolested, but interested; and wearing a look of unconcern. This was a new departure for him, who always fancied that any organization, exclusively female, afforded little opportunity for him to accomplish much along his particular lines.

True, he did not find the material there that he delights to handle, but there was much that be could use to advantage. Women among women are about as loyal to the Devil as they are when there is a man in the case; but their maneuvers are of such a nature that the Devil finds little interest in pursuing them.

After a labored discussion, both pro and con, it was decided to have the program of the afternoon before the business session. There were many whispered protests from those who had sat mute as an oyster during the discussion; but the program progressed, as voted.

There was a paper on "The Moral Influence of Sociology on the Next Generation;" but as the Devil is interested in this generation more than in the next, he did not follow the intricacies of the logic by which certain deductions were reached. He prefers to prove his own theories according to his own syllogisms.

This was followed by a voluminous paper on the "Character of the Byzantine Art as Compared with Other Pre-Raphaelite Painters." With this I was actually bored; however, with the courtesy that the Devil knows so well how to assume, I sat it through, and concealed, as best I could, my immoderate enjoyment of the incongruity of a woman delivering a dissertation on this subject, when she did not know a picture of the Byzantine school from an Egyptian mosaic. Of this the Devil was thoroughly convinced.

When she had finished, there was a storm of applause that came simultaneously from the intellectual "element" and from those whose paramount interest was in the movements of the committee holding forth in the kitchen.

The Devil drew forth his little note-book, and tried to calculate the advantage such a paper would have been to those in attendance, provided they could have comprehended the gist of it; but it was a problem in which the only given quantity was an audience that did not know a Raphael Madonna from a Burne-Jones "Vampire," and he found that he could deduce no results; so he re-adjusted his shoulder-blades to his chair, and his spirit of endurance to the occasion, and listened to the old college-worn, unspeakably-useless, hopelessly-unsuitable discussion, as to whether Bacon or Shakespeare wrote Shakespeare.

When the subject was announced from the chair, in a manner which plainly said, "this question, which has occupied the attention of critics so long, is now about to be settled," and the mistress of research stepped forward to deliver her wise composition, a look of anticipation was transmitted from one listener to another, while the Devil only laughed.

The vanity of mortals is about the most amusing feature of the Devil's work.

However, he listened, with all deference, to some stolen pages from Ignatius Donnelly, read with the gusto of her own language, and heard the fallacious arguments with which she attempted to prove her position, that Bacon was the real author - arguments about as conclusive as the syllogisms with which all early students of logic prove that a feather is heavier than lead, or that a biscuit is better than Heaven.

After all the evidence had been presented, and, in the discussion that followed, the arguments both pro and con been heard, the only tangible point of conclusion was "Who wrote *Shakespeare*"?

The Devil could have settled the question for once and all, had he felt so inclined; for who knows better than he, the author of that grand work? To say that he was amused does not express the half.

There was a certain futility, an impotent aimlessness in their efforts to establish the identity of the author, while the real author, the immortal

Shakespeare, was permitted to remain a sealed book. They could grasp the distinction between two *names*, but the majority of them had no comprehension of the legacy left to literature - and to them - by the divinely inspired "bard of Avon."

There was a sense of relief when the subject was dropped, without a decisive verdict, and the more common-place, common-sense one of "raising children" introduced for discussion. It was a subject that had a practical side at least, which they could grasp and understand.

But even here I was impressed with the same incongruity of things. I knew of my own personal knowledge that those who had most to say on the subject, and those who advanced the most faultless theories in behalf of the coming generation - including that portion of it still unborn - were either those whose offspring could show the most complete record of infantile depravity, or belonged to that ever-increasing host of women who are the living confutation of God's command - childless wives.

I listened with decided interest to the epithets of denunciation that were hurled at mothers by those who were too much occupied in the parental attention which the neighbors' children received, or did not receive, to be cognizant of the fact that their own offspring were sadly neglected.

The charity which He of Nazareth taught, began at home; that which the Devil teaches, begins across the street.

The Devil's observation has been that those who are most enthusiastic in reforming the world, have a household that is sadly in need of their tender ministrations. He might say to them that if they would keep their own backyards clean, it would be an easier matter for the neighbors to do likewise.

But then there would be no avenue to afford an outlet for their nervous energy, and no problems for Women's Clubs to solve - which the Devil decided from his point of view would be a deplorable calamity.

After the question was disposed of to the discomfort of many, and the satisfaction of as many more, there followed the only sensible topic, in the Devil's estimation, of the afternoon - "Current Events."

Pity the Devil, little girl!

There was a response from a large, gaunt woman in a Gibson waist, that took the form (the response, I mean; not the woman or the waist) of a conjecture as to the possible outcome of Queen Alexandra's latest social edict. She further avowed that all England was disappointed over the fate of Shamrock III, but that she was reliably informed that Sir Thomas Lipton was already negotiating for the building of a worthier successor, Shamrock IV.

Then, a woman whose bump of tragedy was abnormally developed, gave a most blood-curdling account of the recent Serbian assassinations.

She descried, in this dark tragedy, the handwriting on the wall, which she interpreted as a warning to the whole world against the seductions of an ambitious and unscrupulous woman.

Following this, was a bulletin by a lady in grey, containing the most authentic account of the Russian peasantry; after which, was set forth by a woman in an extremely high collar, the newest foible of the new king of Spain.

She was succeeded by a woman with a trim-tip nose, who gave the raciest chapters of the Princess Royal of Saxony-Giron episode.

That woman's nose was a study. It possessed the peculiar *tilt* that sniffs a scandal from afar. I thought she ought to have been appointed chairman of the "Smelling Committee."

Referring to the Crown Princess Louise of Saxony - there is a woman after your own heart, Mary. She sold her patrimony for the ignis-fatuus, *Love*!

Love! Ha!-ha!-ha!

While I say she is a woman after your own heart, there is this material difference between you; she was honestly deceived; you are not. She, in her transport, believed that she had grasped the rainbow, Happiness; you know it is a tawdry tinsel. She believed that she saw, just ahead, the purple walls of Paradise; you know it is the fatal mirage, suspended above the burning sands of Sahara!

She believed she had awakened the inward harmonies of life; you know it is a fool's blindness!

And yet, you have sworn to give up "Fame, and Money, and Power, and Virtue, and Honor, and Righteousness, and Truth, and Logic, and Philosophy, and Genius" - all, *all*, for the gleam that you know is of tinsel - for the phantom in the clouds, which you know but lures its victims to madness, and to death!

Surely you enjoy the distinction of being the only living mortal who would, wittingly, make such an exchange.

You must know that I do not speak thus freely to every one. I can afford to be honest with you, because your compact with me is as firm and unalterable as the eternal pillars of Hell!

You could not change it, if you would!

It does even the Devil's soul good to be honest once in a while.

But, to return to the club meeting:

The round-shouldered, intellectual woman, whose duty it was to report the principal event in America, arose and stated that after reading the papers and periodicals, after exhausting the columns of information, she had found but one universal theme, one topic of discussion, one object of public interest - Mary MacLane.

There was a smile, a titter, a subsidence. The Devil became interested at once.

"I find," the oracle stated, "that Mary MacLane has filled more newspaper space than any woman of recent years, the Duchess of Marlborough not excepted. She has probably been more discussed than any woman of her years living today, and for the privilege of being discussed has received thousands of dollars.

"When I probed to find the reason for all this, I learned that she had written the story of herself, and later the story of her friend Annabel Lee. The sole object of the first named was to remind the Devil that she was living, and longing for him to come to her. I read the book, and found nothing in it but a few pretty words, and an undertone of moral perverseness."

"Why, Mrs. Brownfield! Do you mean to say that you have read that disgraceful book, and have the face to speak of it here?" came in a piping voice from an energetic reformer, whose principal occupation, according to her own language, was "getting acquainted with Jesus Christ."

"Certainly," replied Mrs. B. "I fancy I have the same privileges you accord to yourself."

"To be sure! to be sure!" replied the caustic reformer. "I don't see that you are anything ahead, for I found it nothing but rot and abomination."

"I think, ladies," suggested the thin, spare, intellectual woman, who for years had cherished dreams of literary fame, and who, no doubt, envied the short cut made by Mary MacLane. "I really think that you have not fully grasped the meaning of the book. You know it is an allegory, and allegories must never be taken literally. You also know there is a poetic license not accorded to all who wield the pen, and in discussing a book, we must discuss it from all sides," seating herself with the evident satisfaction of having disgorged an accumulation of ideas.

With this, the discussion became general, while the Devil's interest waxed warmer.

The chairman of the philanthropic department had "a word" to say on the subject. She usually had "a word" to say on every subject.

"I think, ladies, that many of us, in this discussion, are at a disadvantage. Now, for my part, I don't know an allegory from a pig-sty; nor poetic license from saloon license or any other kind o' license, but I do know that Mary MacLane's book is not suitable reading for Sunday-school scholars.

"She says a whole lot about wanting to marry the Devil, and I think if she really feels inclined to marry him, she ought to wait, like the rest of her sex, and let the Devil propose to her. He is sure to come, for I think every woman living, at some point in her life, has a chance.

"But since she wrote it, she ought to have prefaced it, so that those of us who are not interested in how a woman makes up to the Devil, would have been warned against reading it. The book does not say that she got the Devil, so it may not be so bad, after all."

The Devil sat mute.

The discussion was getting personal, but he made no manifestation.

"Well," from one of the enthusiastic members, "I think all those who have expressed themselves have read the book in vain. I should pronounce it a perfect gem! The descriptions are magnificently superb; and that cunning little dialogue with the Devil is too cute for anything. She has made him appear so stunning, that most of us would fall in love with him. The book does not say that he is so *awfully* bad: - and oh, when she tells how lonely and unhappy she is, one's heart almost breaks for her!

"She wanted so dreadfully much to make some money and get away from Butte (and which one of us has not felt that way at some time in her life), that now, since she has succeeded, I think she ought to be most awfully praised," reseating herself with the air of a victor who had captured the crown.

"I fail to see," said the philosophical sister from the Home department, "just how the last speaker can eradicate all evil from the book. It is, beyond question, immoral; but immorality often teaches a moral. Mary MacLane says that she believes the Devil rules the world, and it certainly looks that way, at times; consequently she petitions the Devil for material aid.

"The book contains a great many things that the best of us could profit by. There are many parents who think the sole duty they owe to their off-spring is to beget them, and feed them, and clothe them. Mary MacLane has shown that there are higher, nobler duties from a parent to a child, and that the weight of obligation is on the side of the parent.

"She has told us that even children long for congenial surroundings, and that their little lives are shaped for good or for evil almost exclusively by the home influence. You housekeepers who toil from morn till night, that things may be neat and in order, and the family meals on time, could, from reading her book, ask yourselves the question - 'What does it profit, while the heart and mind of my child are hungry?'

"She has told us what the home is without love; how empty is the marriage tie when there is no love to sanctify it. She has told us of the hard, cruel selfishness of the world; of how humanity is faltering for a few kind words - and a little more love.

"There are many lessons in the book that we could each take home. Let us cull the good and leave the evil.

"Where was truth ever unalloyed?"

She resumed her seat amidst loud applause - that characteristic of women that is easily turned to scorn. They encourage theories and lofty ideals, then pull down those who strive to live up to them.

The Devil applauded with the others, for he was beginning to feel a little ugly at the way Mary MacLane was being maligned by these women.

"For my part," in a harsh, rasping voice from the phalanx of refreshment seekers, "the only thing that I could find in the book was that she wanted a man - and wanted him bad!"

Having delivered herself of the burden of an opinion, she resumed her seat with a great deal of satisfaction, remembering that she was the happy possessor of a biped that enjoyed the overwhelming honor of wearing pants.

Calls of "Mrs. Gatewood! Mrs. Gatewood! Let us hear from Mrs. Gatewood!" came from all parts of the room.

A tall, dignified, really handsome woman, of perhaps forty or forty-five years, arose, and was recognized as Mrs. Gatewood by the chairman. She differed from the previous speakers, in that she was calm and deliberate.

"Madame President, and ladies of the Club," she said. "I have read 'The Story of Mary MacLane,' and I must confess that I read it with absorbing interest. To me it is a marvelous book. She is a genius, without doubt.

"A genius, as I understand the term, is one who peers deep into the inmost heart of things, and who has the courage to speak truthfully of what he finds hidden there. Mary MacLane, like a diver, has descended to the bottom of the sea. She tells us it is strewn with grinning skeletons!

"We have been trying to believe the fable that it was covered with mystical coral caves, and peopled with bewilderingly beautiful mermen and mermaids of the sea. We knew this was a delusion; but we tried all the harder to convince ourselves of its truth.

"While I say that Mary MacLane is a genius, I grant you that she is an *unwholesome* genius. We would be better, left alone with our idols - albeit we know they stand on feet of clay!

"I said her book was, to me, a marvelous work. It is! Marvelous, in the fact that a girl of nineteen years could have sounded the depths that she has sounded! Marvelous, in the fact that one so young could have torn aside the curtains, as she has done, and revealed *Truth* in all its hideousness! Marvelous, in the fact that a mere child could have ransacked the charnel-houses of life, and dragged forth their sheeted dead, to be jeered, hooted, and spat upon, by the mob!

"She was deterred neither by *fear* nor *compassion*!

"Her book, coming as it does from a nineteen-year-old girl, presents itself to me with the force of a revelation! Most of us, at that age, saw life through the glow of a wondrous-hued spectrum; she sees it, in all its nakedness, as a 'Pile of Stones and a Barrel of Lime!'

"She says - and no words to me were ever sadder - 'Take anything at any point and deceive yourself into thinking that you are happy with it. But look at it heavily; dig down underneath the layers and layers of rose-colored mists, and you will find that your Thing is a *Pile of Stones and a Barrel of Lime.*'

"Imagine that coming from a nineteen-year-old girl!

"It is astonishing! It is incredible! It is past all conjecture!

"I have asked myself many times, 'How is it possible for one so young to have delved so deep?' She does not disgust or offend me; she *awes*, she *amazes* me!"

Mrs. Gatewood resumed her seat. Many forgot to applaud, so transfixed were they by astonishment. Others stared in utter blankness, not being able to comprehend a word of what she had said. A few, in their hearts, would have liked to endorse Mrs. Gatewood's remarks; but they dared not. They hardly had the courage to confess to themselves, much less to others, the hideous things that were concealed behind the curtain. They shook their heads, smiled, and affected to hug their delusions still more closely to their breasts.

Ah, Mary, you gave those women a good shaking up. Ha!-ha!-ha!!

There was some lively skirmishing amongst the most of them to get their dead under cover. I began to think I had never duly appreciated you, and was just on the point of rising to make a few remarks myself, when the chairman peremptorily remarked that the hour for the business session had arrived.

"We have business of importance," she announced.

And with the announcement I gathered up my bones, my wallet, my metal heart, my hypocrisy - and left.

When I got away, I laughed till my sides ached.

"What fools these mortals be!" - to be sure.

Your very ingenious and captivating -
DEVIL.

*

My Extremely Turbulent Mary: -
   It is a hell of a time you want, little girl -
    A hell of a time, you say:
  You are weary of living, you are weary of dying;
  You are weary of thieving, you are weary of lying;

And long to be lost in a furious whirl -
It's a hell of a time you want!

*

You are tired of eating, you are tired of sleeping -
Your liver itself has grown tired;
Your poor "wooden heart" has worn itself out,
And your "two good legs" can scarce tote you about;
You are tired, so tired, of moping and weeping -
It's a hell of a time you want!

*Your most worshipfully wicked
DEVIL.*

*

My Wild Blatant Mary: -
    Oh, I am a Devil!
    I am immensely pleased with myself tonight.
    I have just accomplished an almost impossible feat!
    If you could see me now, Mary, you would fall in love with me over again, I am sure, for I am truly radiant with my victory.
    Indeed, I am magnificent!
    And what is this almost impossible feat which I have accomplished? You did not know there was anything impossible to the Devil?
    Ah, Mary, I wish you were right.
    I have many parts to play, and the game that promises least to me, is a combat with that arch-enemy of mine - a mother's love. I have been vanquished so many times by this same foe, that I am ready almost to confess myself beaten, at the very outset. Yet, once in a while I am victorious.
    I was today!
    I entered a cottage, where a babe, fresh with the dews of Heaven, lay smiling in its mother's arms. The little mite of humanity that had forced its way into the mother's life was the only tie that held her to the memory of her murdered love; and, again, the only bond that restrained her from a life of sin.
    Six months ago, the tiny eyes that today laughed into hers, were opened under the cloud of dishonor. The little life, conceived in sin, and brought forth in sorrow, was fast becoming a landmark of shame.
    "Why," she wailed, "should I be cursed forever with the evidence of my sin, while he, my partner in crime, goes utterly unscathed?
    "I am a thing for the finger of scorn to point at, while he who should

wear the brand of Cain on his brow - as he does on his soul - walks unspotted among men!

"While every door is closed to me, he stands unchallenged by the world!

"Why should this little life be thrust upon me - me only - to be a millstone about my neck, while he who is equally guilty with me goes forth untouched by the breath of disgrace?

"Ah, thus it is with the *man*, and the creature who bears the 'plague-tainted name' - *woman!*"

I only laughed, and reminded her of the time when she listened to my voice without remonstrance, and yielded to my temptation without fear of consequences. I taunted her with the memory of those days when sin was sweet, and the Devil was a generous pay-master; when she accepted my caricature of love, and yielded herself to its delirium.

Poor fool that she was!

I haunted her with the memory of all that she had lost - honor, hope, virtue, reputation, home, friends, love, and - more than all - her own inner consciousness of purity.

The ecstasy of her sin, the bliss of love, that made her sin so sweet, I have changed to the gall of bitterness!

The path of sin, where all the allurements of love were spread out before her in one grand panorama of beauty, I have transformed into the cold stony path of the transgressor. The rose petals that strewed her path have withered and died, or been blown away on the wings of the wind, and only the thorns remain. The dews of spring have been congealed into winter's frozen shroud.

I upbraided her for her folly.

I mocked her with the spectre of that dream which made her sin so ravishing. I derided her loveless life, by dangling before her eyes that scene of youthful folly, where Love was made a living sacrifice on his own crimson-dyed altar!

I tortured her with the pangs of Hell, until, in desperation, she fled from the scene of my persecution.

She was asked to return home - back to the fireside of the old Indiana farm-house - but the conditions stipulated were that she should return *alone.*

Should she desert the child of her love? the little waif that had come into her life, because of that love? the only thing that lessened the gloom of that departed love? the little soul that she had called into existence?

Should she place this wee, helpless creature, born in the image of its mother, upon the world's door-step?

Again and again I taunted her.

I reproached her with the evidence of her sin. I cursed her for her folly. I mocked her crushed and broken spirit, until, frenzied, she laid the child at the feet of the cold, cold world - and fled!

I had won! Ha!-ha!-ha!

Wonderful Devil that I am, to counterfeit the very sacredness of Heaven, and wring from a trusting woman the sacrifice of her womanhood; and then - victory of victories! - to make her abandon the innocent babe, born of this accursed sacrifice!

Ah, this is my recompense, and I shall accept it without stint.

Poor foolish woman, to be led by the Devil - and then kicked by the Devil into Hell!

Will the fireside that you bought with the price of your child warm the depths of your desolate heart? Will the miles and miles that stretch away to the east, and offer you a resting-place in the home of your youth, separate you from the memory of your child? Will the sacredness of family ties, by which you are surrounded, enable you to forget the bond of *motherhood*?

Can you ever shut out from your sight the helplessness of those two little outstretched arms, that plead their cause in their own mute way?

Will this tragedy which was enacted in a western mining town ever haunt you less?

The Devil will not be idle, but with the help of you, Mary MacLane, and your peripatetic philosophy, will transform it, for the edification of others, into a comedy.

There is no sin; there is no shame; for all was done through the blind, blundering sentiment of *love*.

The Devil rejoices in the fact that Love is blind; he can thus lead the little god into any snare he may choose to prepare for him.

Come, Mary, you can be of inestimable service to the Devil.

Go before him. Imbue the minds of the young and unsuspecting with the spirit of your philosophy.

Proclaim from the housetops the superfluousness of marriage. Convert the world to your so-called theory of love - and the Devil will do the rest.

But what, little girl, will we do with the *child*?

Yours enthusiastically,
THE DEVIL.

*

My Little Cynic: -

Remember, Mary, that every "bronze-and-copper beam" has its moat;

every diamond its flaw; every pearl its fleck; and every sunset its hand-breadth of grey, that shall grow and grow and grow - until the purple and gold are swallowed up in darkness!

Your self-sufficient
DEVIL.

*

My Own Trusting Mary: -

I am distressed: I am outwitted; I am routed!

I have an adversary, who rises in his strength and grandeur, and I seem to be unable to cope with him.

He is young; he is human; he is natural; yet the wiles of the Devil are not sufficient to draw him from his position.

He defies me.

In the face of the world, despite the magnitude of my forces, he dares to raise his voice against me.

He is utterly lost to me, I fear; but, could I only cause him to stumble, his host of followers might turn in confusion. I am not often thwarted, but resistance is the only weapon that causes me to turn and flee. That is the only argument that I cannot meet.

Had I but a delusion, an hallucination, with which to weaken his power of resistance, I might, perhaps, defeat him. Could I only fabricate some false doctrine, build up some false shrine, raise up some false god, I might hope to conquer him.

Could I only blind him with some new theory; weave about him some spell that might stupefy his energy; breathe upon his senses the sweet in-toxication of my allurements - in his helpless state, I might overpower him.

I shall now try *woman* - that strange combination of mystery and light, strength and frailty, hope and uncertainty; who becomes at once the mediative influence between man and his Creator, and, again, the very incarnation of myself!

*

When the fair form of woman, to solace man's heart,
Was fashioned and formed by old Mulciber's art,
The crowned heads of Heaven were summoned to lavish
Every charm and attraction, ere woman he'd finish.
Some gave to her beauty; some, god-like affection:
Their united endowments just made her *perfection*.
'Bove all the rich gifts that each goddess bestowed,

The richest, 'tis said, to the gods she owed.
A casket it is, and contains the rich treasure
Of woman's rare love, and in infinite measure.
When the seal has been broken, and the treasure revealed,
No man who has seen it could wish it were sealed!

*

Yes, I shall try *woman*!

It is woman, who, from the foundation of the world, has ever wrought man's utter undoing!

When I first planned the fall, I did it through the subtlety of woman. Kings have crossed swords to win her favor; nations have plunged into war at her command; kingdoms have been sold for her smiles, and empires have followed in the wake of her fascination; states have been wrecked by her witchery, and history has been shaped according to her fancy.

The destiny of the world is folded in the hollow of her hand!

She is always a trump card; and when played by the Devil - ha!-ha!-ha!! - the Devil always wins the trick.

Woman is my trump of trumps - and woman I shall play!

He is human.

He is in the glory of young manhood. He knows the meaning of my seductions, and the blind, compelling force of my captivity. In time past he wavered at the whisper of my promises, and sipped at the fountain of my pleasures. He halted before the throne of my deity; but, as one who suddenly awakens from a dream, he gathered the strength of his convictions, and forced his way beyond the secret scope of my temptations.

To the spell of my subsequent allurements he has proved impervious. In the majesty of his strength he defies me and my army.

Verily, I am persuaded that he does not stand of his own strength, but is upheld by that Supreme Power which I have never been able to overcome. Flesh, alone, is weak, and prone to do evil; and it is only when I find it supported by the strength of my first adversary that I am unable to effect its downfall.

I can never destroy, I can never paralyze *that* Power! Could I only clothe it in my own light, I might use it to my own purposes.

To this end, *woman* I shall employ.

To those who are my most faithful followers, and least likely to betray me, I have insinuated that the Master himself is but the product of man's folly and woman's perfidy.

When man is lost to reason, and woman is lost to virtue, the Devil laughs at the consequences.

What role shall she assume?

Shall she pass meek-eyed before him, and steal her way into his heart through the innocence of the Vestal Virgin? Shall she smile at him from beneath the confirmation veil? Shall she melt his heart to pity through the guise of the Magdalen? Shall she dally him with the mischievous game of a coquet? Or shall she dazzle him with the revelation of woman as she is?

Which would most surely and most swiftly win?

Up, little Mary MacLane, I have need of thee.

Do thou prepare to do the Devil's bidding!

Yours in haste,
THE DEVIL.

*

My Visionary Mary: -

And what do you think Love is, little girl?

A bird-of-paradise which you sought to lure into your net by the careless abandon of your Portrayal, or which you hoped, serpent-like, to charm, until you might creep near enough to throw salt upon his tail?

In your flights of wayward fancy, your eyes beheld him poised high, high above you!

> *You gazed, till he seemed but a speck,*
> *Careering the ether of Heaven.*

You were dazzled by the splendor of his plumage - an inheritance which has always been the envy of his kind. From behind your high board fence, you watched this beautiful thing with an intensity that filled you with a desire to hold it in your hand - to possess it!

You measured the distance between your own circumscribed sphere and the dizzy height at which your bird-of-paradise was poised. Just as you were beginning to realize that this dazzling creature was forever beyond your reach, lo! he descended!

He came nearer, nearer, nearer, until you could even distinguish the emerald from the gold on his breast; and the vermilion from the sapphire on his wings!

You trilled to him, in imitation of the song of his mate, but he deigned not an answering note.

"What, oh what can I do, to bring him nearer?" you exclaimed. "I might climb to the top of my high board fence and beckon to him, but would he ever descend within the reach of my arms? I might scatter crumbs on the sand and barrenness, to tempt him from his lofty height, but would he ever circle low enough to discover them? I might build him a nest on the top of the telegraph pole in front of 'this house,' but would he ever seek its warmth and tenderness?

"I must have him; but how can I secure him?"

You thought and pondered, and finally wondered if even a bird-of-paradise could be deceived by ornament.

You arrayed yourself in gewgaws and tinsel, to simulate the object which you coveted. So adorned, you mounted the housetop, and spread your glittering trappings to the sun! You whistled such a note as you thought might emanate from his own emerald throat.

He halted in his flight, and, poised in the blue ether of Heaven, he vouchsafed to you one look, then - "tuk" to his wings!

Yours compassionately,
THE DEVIL.

*

My Most Astonishing, Unaccountable Mary: -

I feel, in view of the intimacy which has sprung up between us in the course of these letters, that you are interested in all that I do. However that may be, I do know that I experience a peculiar delight in confiding to you my movements.

Today I went calling, and even there I learned something of importance concerning yourself. Now, don't smile, and fancy that I am becoming frivolous, because I chose to call in the neighborhood; for, in order to keep up with the "smart set," I must do as they do, and it keeps me "a-humping!"

I stopped first at Mrs. Ambergris'.

"Oh, how do you do, Mrs. Deville? I haven't seen you since Mrs. Youngblood's dance!" taking the tips of my two fingers as gingerly as though they had been two hot chestnuts.

"Quite well, thank you!" I replied, with the patronizing air that the Devil knows how to assume advantageously. "I have thought of you so often, and wondered if you had heard that the Youngbloods had parted."

"Parted?" gasped Mrs. Ambergris, "and all the society people their guests not two weeks ago! It seems incredible. How did you hear it?"

"Mrs. Hornblower is my authority, and she told me that Mrs. Gabbs told her."

"Yes, I have the whole thing, now," gloated Mrs. A. "Mrs. Brown told Mrs. Gabbs, Mrs. Doolittle told Mrs. Brown, and Mrs. Newcome told Mrs.

Doolittle. I know, because Mrs. Newcome's and Mrs. Youngblood's hired girls are sisters. They always go home together every night, and that is how the Newcomes and the Youngbloods happen to know so much about each other's affairs. For my part, I never did like Mrs. Youngblood, any way. People have wondered for a long time how she could dress and entertain as she does. I always thought there was something strange about it myself. Ambergris' salary is $27.95 a month more than Youngblood's, and I can't afford to do the things she does. We could all give dances and dress fine, if -" with a meaning wink of her black, snappy eyes.

"That's right; that's right," I repeated deploringly, at the same time nodding my head in compliance with all that she said.

"The little minx!" exclaimed Mrs. Ambergris, who was making the most of her opportunity to satisfy her innate love for scandal and her particular enjoyment at the downfall of a woman. "And to think that she has been received into society here, and the ladies have been so nice to her. Well, I'll *freeze* her the next time I see her! I'll at least let her know that Caroline Ambergris has found out what she is!"

"Oh, don't mention what I said to you," I returned apologetically, knowing that that was the surest way to advertise it. "I didn't mean to say anything that would reflect on Mrs. Youngblood. I have always been very fond of her," in an insinuating tone that Mrs. A. understood, and was secretly pleased to note.

"Oh, must you be going?" she said, following me to the door. "I am so glad you came, and so thankful to have learned the straight of the Youngblood affair. Now, do come again, won't you? Why, I do believe that is Mrs. Youngblood driving up to my gate, now."

"Yes, that is she," I replied, in a conciliatory tone; at the same time drawing Mrs. A.'s attention to Mrs. Y.'s handsome carriage wrap. "'Speak of the devil,' etc. -"

"Why, how do you do, Mrs. Ambergris - and Mrs. Deville?" came in a sweet, gentle tone from the lady in question, as her carriage drew up in front of the gate.

In the meantime I had been observing Mrs. A., who inwardly felt that she would like to cut her, but who realized that the gorgeous new hat which Mrs. Youngblood was wearing deserved some recognition.

"Quite well, thank you! And how are you? Won't you get out?" she called, most patronizingly, as, with furtive scrutiny, she observed that Mrs. Y. was sporting a magnificent new ostrich boa. I saw with satisfaction that the Youngblood stock had advanced proportionately.

"Oh, no, thank you!" she replied. "I haven't time; I just stopped to say good-bye."

"Oh, you are going away?"

"Just for a trip. Papa sent me an invitation to accompany him and Alberta on a trip through Yellowstone Park, and the invitation was accompanied by a generous check. That is just like papa; he is always sending me something."

"How charming!" I ventured, for Mrs. A. was too much overcome to recognize the demands of courtesy.

"Yes, it is. I am sorry I did not get around to see you, but I have been so busy, getting ready. I have taken this opportunity to see those whom I felt I could not leave without a word, at least. How fortunate that I can see you both here!"

"How perfectly delighted I am to know that you are going to have such a splendid trip!" chimed Mrs. A., while I saw ill-concealed envy darken her countenance.

After a few more stereotyped expressions, good-byes were said. The lady in the carriage was borne away, oblivious of the fact that opprobrium had been hurled at her; the lady of the house gathered up her spleen, and went back to the stool of her discontent, while the Devil pursued his hypocritical course.

Presently I met a pair of society "buds," who were discussing a member of their set.

"Oh," said one, "I think Miss Swann is perfectly lovely! She wears the swellest gowns, and always looks so stunning!"

"Yes, her new hat has six tips on it, and they did not cost a cent less than three dollars apiece. But she has an awfully ugly mouth; don't you think so?"

"Oh, to be sure! No one would ever call her a beauty, with that mouth - and her sallow complexion."

I passed on.

I called at this house, and at that; and my varied experiences were very similar to those already recorded.

Presently I was ushered into a little parlor, whose peace and comfort I had so often coveted. This was a door from which none were ever turned away. Its mistress may, at times, have entertained "angels unawares," but I am sure that she often harbored the Devil in disguise.

Agents and peddlers received no rebuffs here, and, when dismissed, were dismissed in a gentle and forbearing manner. I always stopped at this door, because, in the most unsuspecting manner, its mistress gave me a great many pointers.

I had succeeded in coaxing from her the name of the latest recipient of her charity, as well as the names of those whose condition she anticipated bettering, when the unmistakable rap of the female peddler was heard.

"Can you spare me a little of your time?" she asked, in a most persuasive tone, as my hostess opened the door, and extended to her a mute invitation to enter.

"I have here an assortment of toilet articles," she said, and immediately began to display the mysterious contents of the little satchel, much like a half-size dress-suit case, which she carried.

"I carry everything for the beautifying of the face and form. 'Orris Root Paste,' for the teeth: 'Magnolia Cream,' for the complexion; 'Pomegranate Lotion,' for the lips; 'Extract of Rosemary,' for the hair; 'Heart of Sea-shell Powder,' for the ears; 'Belladonna Pupil Dilator,' for the eyes; 'Black Diamond Pencil,' for the eye-brows; 'Carbon Wax,' for the eye-lashes; 'White Hawthorn Salve,' for the hands; 'Ruby Dust,' for the finger-nails; 'Topaz Enamel,' for the toe-nails," producing innumerable jars, boxes, tubes, and bottles, from the depths of the little satchel, which I eyed, now, as a truly miraculous object.

Our hostess took each article as it was handed to her, and after a dutiful inspection, passed it over to me.

"The goods are all warranted," continued the agent, "they have been duly tried and endorsed by the woman whose name they bear, Mary MacLane."

With this, I almost started from my chair; and my first thought was, "What will she do next?"

"Yes," continued the lady, "we carry everything for beautifying the person, and for preserving the beauty one naturally possesses. There is no longer any need, or I might more properly say, any *excuse* for a homely woman."

I became intensely interested; for, try as I may, I cannot conceive even the least liking for a plain woman.

"Now, this, 'Magnolia Cream,' is what Mary MacLane uses for her complexion, and she has a face of 'madonna-like sweetness.' She says so herself. There has been a most wonderful transformation in her since she began the use of this cream.

"You remember also that she said she had naturally beautiful hair. Still, she uses 'Extract of Rosemary' three times a week, rubbing it well into the scalp; and now her hair trails on the floor, and envelops her like a circular.

"This," running on like Tennyson's "Brook," "is the 'Mary MacLane Massage Cream,' and -"

"I am not so sure," interrupted my hostess, "that the name of Mary MacLane would lend much character to your goods."

"O yes, madame! Maybe you do not know the lady."

"I only know her through her book, and I've no desire to cultivate her further, unless I might point out to her the evil of her ways," replied my hostess, with a righteous toss of her head.

"Of course my goods have nothing to do with her book, madame."

"Then she has quit writing books, and gone to manufacturing face cream and the like? Well, she has developed more sense than I thought her capable of."

"She has probably realized that nature needed a few artificial appliances before she could capture the man-devil," I ventured, with the demureness of a self-righteous saint.

"Well, you know we must assist nature," continued the lady. "Now, here is a jar of 'Monumental Cream,' a delightfully smooth and bland compound. It is warranted to produce, in an incredibly short space of time, a most beautifully rounded throat and chest; and this, a bottle of 'Liquid Alabaster,' goes with it, for removing all scars and blemishes.

"This," displaying a curious little article, the like of which I had never seen before, "is the 'Bust Plumper,' an electrical device for enlarging the bust; and is accompanied by a pamphlet giving valuable directions. It is especially recommended by Mary MacLane, for she is no longer driven to the extremity of arranging nine cambric handkerchiefs in the bosom of her dress, in order to obtain that graceful outward curve which is sought after by all true femininity. You, madame," to my hostess, "would find this invaluable, as you seem to be rather thin-chested."

"I have neither the time nor the money to devote to such things. I am always busy, looking after the Lord's work."

I only fancied that the Lord might love her a little better, and might point to her with more pride, it she could only make herself a little more attractive. My hostess is a dear, kind-hearted little woman, and I felt thankful that the Lord loved her, for the Devil could not.

Does that please you, little girl?

"What else have you?" I inquired, more interested in the transformation of Mary MacLane than in the stock of goods.

"I have here a liquid paste, called 'Psyche's Bridal Veil,' that imparts to the veriest parchment complexion the bloom of youth; 'Angelica Abdominal Ointment,' for reducing the size of the abdomen; corn salve; 'Medicated Sea-foam' soap; 'Ramrod Corsets' - everything."

"This," exhibiting a nondescript affair, which resembled a collapsed water-bag, "is a new thing, and fills a long-felt want. It is an inflated rubber bustle. Mary MacLane says she would look like a flap-jack without hers.

"One could, by the persistent use of 'Monumental Cream,' develop a natural bustle, but that would not be advisable as bustles are likely to go out of style at any moment. To be sure, it could be removed by 'Angelica Abdominal Ointment,' but it would require much time and patience."

Our voluble agent then exhibited a ghostly looking thing, with eyes, nose, and a most frightful, grinning mouth, which she called a "Juliet Facial Mask," and informed us it was to be worn during sleep. She said it would perform miracles. I asked her if it would remove the *tan* from leather.

She said it would.

It was truly a wonderful thing; but I wouldn't like my wife (if I had one) to wear such a thing during sleep. I am sure it would give me a nervous turn. "A hint to the wise," etc. -

She next exhibited what looked like a baby's rattle, only it did not rattle, but which she said was an "Anti-Crow-foot Roller," and would also perform miracles. It would take the crinkles out of waffle-irons; for I asked her.

"I have also a book, entitled 'The Physical Woman,'" rattled our irrepressible agent, "explaining how to acquire a graceful carriage, a straight back, and hips any size one should desire. This has also been of inestimable value to Mary MacLane, who has now discarded her moreen petticoat altogether.

"We have, however, the 'Junoesque Hip-pads,' for those who are not persevering enough to follow the instructions. And here," producing a particularly ugly thing, which I was sure was a "rat" for the hair, "is something no woman of your build, especially during this era of short skirts, should be without - the 'Perfection False Calf.'

"It is to be adjusted thus," suiting the action to the words (the Devil held his breath, but, I am compelled to admit, did not glance up at the ceiling just at that particular moment), "and it is warranted not to slip, or get out of position. Mary MacLane says she would not be without a pair for the world."

"Oh my!" and I gave a gasp that brought forth solicitations from my hostess in regard to the state of my health.

Heretofore, little girl, I had fancied that you were free from all these frauds, that, at times, delude even me; but this demonstrates the fact that you are the Devil's own child.

Have you so soon fallen into the follies of your sex?

Have those two good legs, that once you were proud to own, been stuffed to appease this last phase of your vanity? Of course they are your legs, and you can do with them as you please; you may dazzle mankind, and become the envy of womankind because of their generous measurements, but, for the love of Hell and the Devil, remove your "Perfections" before I arrive.

"This" (Jehoshaphat! more to follow!), holding up a bottle of perfectly colorless liquid, "is the most wonderful discovery of the age, and is something I sell almost every where I stop. It is 'Aladdin's Magic Hair Curler,' and will, instantly upon application, produce in the straightest of hair, the most beautiful and apparently natural waves. No more curling-irons, kid-curlers, curl-papers, etc., to disgust your husbands."

Disgust your husbands! *Hully gee*!

"This," producing a bottle so similar in appearance to the one she had just exhibited that the possibility of their being mistaken one for the other made me shudder, after I learned that the second bottle contained "Hair Vamoser," a compound warranted not only to remove all superfluous hair, but to absolutely destroy the follicles, so that they could not possibly sprout again.

Picture the catastrophe, Mary, if you, in your haste, should mistake "Hair Vamoser" for "Aladdin's Magic Hair Curler" - and you with such beautiful hair, too.

It almost gives me heart failure to contemplate such a thought!

Promise me, Mary, that you will keep one bottle up-stairs, and the other down-stairs. It would be safer.

"Then, I have the 'Little Cupid' garters," clattered the unabashed agent. (Holy Moses! I wonder that all women are not lunatics!) "These garters are particularly recommended by Mary MacLane. They are 'the red, red' quality, and are magnetically charged."

"I have also the 'Hesperides' perfumes, and -"

"I don't believe I care for anything in your line today," said my hostess. "They are all very good, of course; but I do not care for them."

After futile protestations of their miraculous merits, she was finally persuaded to replace her store, but not without many reminders that this was the first time that the "Mary MacLane goods" had been offered for sale. True, she remembered that there was a Mary MacLane brand of tabasco sauce, as well as a similar brand of cigars; but nothing along the line of her goods.

At last she was induced to click her little satchel, with all its wonder-working devices on the inside, and with that seraphic smile which all her profession cultivate, she graciously inquired the name of the lady next door - and was gone.

I sat speechless!

I could see nothing but bewildering visions of inflated bustles, hip-pads, false calves, bust plumpers, grinning facial masks, etc., and, horror of horrors! all this paraphernalia attached to the person of Mary MacLane!

I now know how to sympathize with the astonished bridegroom, who, upon being conducted to the bridal chamber, was puzzled as to whether he was expected to sit up with the part of his bride which occupied the chair, or to retire with the part which had gone to bed.

Yours in perplexity,
THE DEVIL.

*

On the Lake, Hell, 1903.

My Own Unspeakable Mary: -

You have besought me to come to you. Listen, little girl, while I tell you a story.

Once I went in all my majesty, in all my strength, in all my power, in all my adorable wickedness, to a woman "young and all alone."

She was beautiful as the dawn, passionless as snow, ethereal as an angel! Her fair soul, crowned with a halo of virgin purity, looked out through eyes of infinite trust.

I lifted her in my arms and bore her away - far away from her weary, wretched Nothingness.

"Whither are we going, Kind Devil?" she asked.

"To the Vale of Yellow Light," I answered, "where grows the mystic Tree of Knowledge, watered by the spring of Love!"

"And is this vale far, Kind Devil?"

"Far, very far; over 'the green wetness and sweetness,'" I said.

"What grows in this vale, Kind Devil, besides the mystic Tree of Knowledge, watered by the spring of Love?"

"Ah, mint, and white hawthorn, and myrtle, and rose, and hyacinth, and jasmine, and blue-bells,' I answered.

"When will we reach this vale, Kind Devil?"

"When the sun touches the meridian, and the light is golden yellow."

And even as I spake, there was wafted to us over the heaven-kissing hills, a breath of myrtle and rose, and a wonderful light of transfiguration descended upon us! Under this light, "that never was on land or sea," her young woman's body shone resplendent - a thing of beauty, and light, and love!

Aphrodite, when she rose from the sea, was not more than dazzling than she, clothed, as she was, in the mist of the morning, with beads of dew in her hair, and her bare feet of ivory whiteness resting in a bed of wet blue-bells.

I led her to a bank of purple hyacinth - and lo! the mystic Tree of Knowledge, watered by the spring of Love, bent above it!

We were together, she and I, in the gold light "for days - for days!" But there was no marking of time, there. In the Vale of Yellow Light, "one day is as a thousand years, and a thousand years as one day!"

"Do you love me, sweet Devil?" she asked

"Ay, from the depths of my metal heart!" I answered. Ha!-ha!-ha!!

She turned her fawn-like eyes to me, their look of boundless faith changed into one of uncertain bewilderment.

Then, summoning the most potent magic of my art, I cast upon her such a spell of rapturous abandonment, that she exclaimed:

"O glorious Devil! clasp me; crush me; consume me with hot love! Blister me with your burning lava kisses; wrap me round so tight with your 'strong steel arms' that my quivering woman's body shall all but break in your embrace! Send such a cutting ecstasy through my supersensitive nerves as shall threaten to snap them in twain!

"For this I have given up 'Fame, and Money, and Power, and Virtue, and Honor, and Righteousness, and Truth, and Logic, and Philosophy, and Genius!' Make it worth the price, O Devil!"

"And the children you will bear me - will they be human, angel, god, or devil?"

"Devil! *devil!* - born in the image of yourself, O marvelous Devil!"

"Can your bear it - the infinity of love?" I asked.

"Yes! yes! Abate it nothing - though I die!"

Then I touched her young woman's body with fire - the Devil's fire - and she fell in a swoon like death! Not death, though; but seeming death, from an ecstasy more poignant than pain!

Here, I drew a canopy of clouds about us; for the things I said to her and the things she said to me, on that bank of purple hyacinth, under the mystic Tree of Knowledge, watered by the spring of Love - must never be revealed! Dost thou like the picture, Mary?

Yours ecstatically and sulphurously,
THE DEVIL.

*

Nethermost Chamber of Hell.
Midnight, 1903.

My Own Benighted Mary: -

Rest! Rest!

Ah, there is no rest for the Devil!

God made the world and the glory thereof in six days, and rested on the seventh.

All things whatsoever rest, except the Prince of Darkness!

The days come and go, and nature lies down to sleep.

The trees of the forest chant a lullaby to the flowers that nod in the field, and to the tender blades of grass that nestle at their feet.

The waves of the ocean draw the shades of night about them, and rock to sleep the myriad forms of life that throng its mighty waters.

The beasts of the field, that are not tortured by man's brutality, lie down to nature's rest and refreshment.

Almost with the setting of the sun, the weariness of childhood is lost in balmy sleep.

The pure in heart lift up their souls in thankfulness at eventide, and invoke God's watchful care for another night, then lay them down to peaceful slumbers.

The wayward, whose transgressions have been many, can thus escape the spectre of rebuke; and the sin-besotted creature, who plods his way - a menace to the world, a reproach to the Devil - has also this recourse from remorse.

The world sleeps, but the Devil must press on!

I was driven out from the glory of light, and condemned to live always beyond its halo.

Darkness became my legacy!

I have not despised my fallen estate; and the darkness which I am doomed to inherit, has blessed my labors and added strength to my kingdom.

When the curtain of night envelops you, little girl, and myriad voices (mosquitoes) chant the lullaby of sleep in your ears, there is no rest for me. There is no deep solitude to tempt me from my labors; no roseate couch to woo me into slumber, and to refresh my metal heart with the inspiration of a dream; no kind, unconscious sleep, in which, for a time, I might forget even myself; no gentle hand to draw the veil of oblivion around me for a season!

No; from day to day, year to year, eternity to eternity, I am ever present with myself!

I am forever confronted with the blackness!

The horror of my surroundings is constantly before me. The victims of my fiendish subtlety are never beyond my sight. The ravings of the damned, swelling in one mighty requiem, beat constantly upon my ears. The writhings of their agony rise always before me. The holocaust of Hell spreads its lurid glare unceasingly around me!

There is no escape.

Hell is my throne; and I am doomed to live forever under the weight of its crown!

Eternity is spread out before me - an eternity of *Hell*!

Can you picture, Mary MacLane, what this is?

No; the finite mind cannot grasp the meaning of eternity, to say nothing of an eternity of Hell.

It is Hell, where all the evil tendencies of earth are culminated; where every restraining influence is withdrawn; where sin, in all its hideousness, goes on repeating itself forever and forever!

Can you imagine a state where kindness, charity, sympathy, have never entered? Where God's infinite spirit of love - an unconscious chain, binding together the creatures of earth - hovers not? Where the human soul, so poisoned - so besotted - so distorted - so damned - lives on forever in the depths of its own damnation? Where cruelty is more cruel, and the rod of the oppressor is more oppressive? Where suffering is never relieved?

Where an eternity of punishment is meted out to those who have transgressed the laws of right?

I was the first who transgressed, and this is my inheritance.

I delight forever in the torments of Hell!

I am glorified by the abject abasement of those whom I have led to their own destruction; I am exalted by the sight of their agony; I am rejoiced by the sound of their wailing; I am ravished by the echo of their remorse; until, in exultation, I turn and wreak upon them the flood of my hatred and my vengeance!

I love to see them struggle, struggle - then fall lower!

I triumph in the means which Heaven has given me to make Hell a place of eternal damnation.

When I am surfeited with devilish glee I crucify again these wretched souls to vivify my fiendish enjoyment.

I stretch their quivering forms upon the rack of torture and bind them more firmly in the cankering chains of my bondage. I quicken their sensibilities afresh with the fire of my devilish purposes, and leave them to vent the fury of their torture upon each other.

This is Hell - *in Hell*!

Between earth and Hell I have hung a curtain of heavenly enchantment. I have made the pathway appear like one unbroken dream of delight. The pitfalls I have spread over with a carpet of flowers. The tumultuous roar of this pandemonium I have muffled till the unsuspecting might mistake it for the ripple of some distant melody.

Hell must remain in Hell; and no sight or sound escape therefrom to thwart my purposes on earth.

Ah, the Devil is a clever dissembler!

You would like, little Mary MacLane, to join the host of his followers on earth; but would you like to draw aside the curtain and enter the Hell beyond?

Would you like the Devil to love you for a season - then curse you for an eternity?

Would you like to bask in the rainbow hues of his earthly kingdom - then sink into endless night?

Would you crucify your soul for a fleeting pleasure that will haunt you forever and forever?

Would you sell your soul to the Devil for a day, for the which he will despise you through eternity?

You have said that you would! Ha!-ha!-ha!

Yours sincerely and diabolically,
THE DEVIL.

*

My Little Will O' the Wisp: -

Forgive me, Mary, for my thoughtlessness. I may at times seem harsh, but you must know that I am never too harsh to open my heart to you in a flood of pleasure and delight.

At times, in the heat of my impatience, I have almost clasped you in my arms! I have almost brushed the dews from your maiden cheek and have almost sipped the wine from your ruby lips!

In my fitful imagination, I have almost felt the glow of your young woman's body, and have almost wrapped you round with my strong steel arms! I have almost drunk the perfume of your languorous breath, and have *almost* caught the waves of sensuous delight that dash themselves against the windows of your soul!

In times of meditation I have chafed at the restraint with which circumstances and pressing duties have enthralled me; and, in fancy, I have almost claimed you!

In dreams which were not all dreams, I have snatched you from the world; and have led you to the throne of my habitation; crowned you with the aureole of my glory; armed you with the sceptre of my power; decked you with the jewels of the firmament; arrayed you in the splendor of the morning; worshiped you with the adoration of the spirit world; and loved you with the intensity of the *Devil*!

In fancy, I have basked in the sunlight of your presence; I have lavished upon you the wealth of Parnassus; I have laid at your feet the trophies of the ages; and have studded your crown with the gems of the Milky Way!

I have anointed you with the perfume of Hesperides; have poured upon your altars the incense of the gods; and have caught the music of the spheres, and translated it for your delight!

I have poured out to you the rapture of my boundless soul; have compassed time and space with the limit of your wish; and have arrayed infinity in the rainbow tints of beauty for your delectation!

In thought, I have gone to you on the wings of the moonbeam, and have whispered to you the poetry of love in tones so soft, so melodic, and so enchanting that your soul was almost moved to answer the refrain.

I have caught the rays of the sunbeam as it flashed upon your vision; and, in its matchless radiance, have hung upon your slumberous eyes until their infinite depths seemed almost melted into love.

I have followed the hide-and-seek of the echo till I *almost* caught the whispered word my soul would win from you.

I have gone to you in the rosy dawn, and have painted upon your soul the pictures which *almost* wrapped you in the spell of my enchantment.

I have lurked in the twilight shadows, and have followed your presence through the purple afterglow of day, till our ways seemed almost merged in one, and you, through all eternity, were *almost* my own.

Again, in eager hope and expectation, I have mounted the chariot of the wind, as, laden with the fragrance of the meadows, it kissed your ruddy cheek or toyed in wanton sport with your silken tresses; and have *almost* felt your bosom heave with the ecstasy of my presence!

In riotous thought tonight my fancy almost claims you; my arms almost embrace you; and my lips almost press yours!

I almost catch the light that burns within your eyes; I almost feel the thrill that passes through your form and I *almost*, ALMOST chain your soul in the bondage of a long, compelling kiss!

My wild impatience is becoming more than I can bear, so speed the day when you may no longer be "so near and yet so far."

Your loving and impatient
DEVIL.

*

The Infernal Mansion.
Fall of Eve, 1903.

My Own Intense Mary: -

Tonight I stood in the ruby twilight.

It was the hour of the grand transfiguration of the sun, when he gazes, at the same time, on the past eternity and shimmers in the head-light of the future.

'Twas the hour of the sunset's golden death!

The full round moon was just peeping over the hills of the eastern horizon, as if she were loth to show her face in the presence of the majestic king of day.

Gradually, and imperceptibly, the ruby had turned to purple and the gold to silver white; though the one tall, spire-like butte which stands to the south still wore his tip of fire, like a flaming torch in the sky!

Like the great eye of the sun, I can look backward into the deep shadows of the past, and at the same time penetrate with my prophetic sense, far, far into the realm of the future.

As I gazed into the years that are to come I saw a Soul, naked and shivering. It was creeping along in the moonlight like a hunted thing!

I quickened my pace, and walked almost beside it.

It was a Soul, stripped of its robes of purity, and branded with the marks of shame!

Presently it halted in a lone, deserted space.

The moonlight fell full upon it, and I saw it lift its white hands in supplication, then wring them in an agony of despair! I heard its cry of bitter anguish, as it fell prone upon a little mound, overspread with rough, sharp stones.

It was the grave of a woman's honor - the grave in which she and her Soul, one ghostly night, buried her young Womanhood, with no watchers but the moon, three pale stars - and myself.

Tonight, the same moon, the same three pale stars, and myself, looked down upon that Soul in its travail.

"Oh, that a Soul could die! Oh, that a Soul could die!" it wailed.

"Why dost thou weep, lost Soul?" I asked.

It turned its eyes, burning with the light of immortality, full upon me, and cried:

"O Devil, Devil! grant me one boon - one boon, if thou can'st."

"And what is this boon thou cravest, Soul?"

"Death! death! O Devil! *Oblivion! oblivion!*" it cried, its white arms outstretched in agonized entreaty.

"Soul, dost thou not know thou can'st not die?"

"O Devil! summon all thy strength, all thy power, and smite me - smite me, O Devil! - till I needs must die!"

"Soul, did I sear thee with the branding-irons of Hell, till thou wast shriveled up to nothing, thou should'st still live!"

Oh! the wail of that lost Soul, as it fell back upon the grave of the thing it had murdered! The moon, as if affrighted, hid her face behind a cloud, and the three pale stars trembled!

"Then go away from me, O mocking Devil," it cried, "and leave me alone - alone with my dead! Taunt me not with the memory of that day when this child of my bosom was slain - this child of Innocence and Truth."

"Why art thou here alone, Soul? Where is the woman, thy incarnation, that she is weeping not for her dead?"

"In the halls of revelry, tonight. She chided me because I would not go. Oh! I could not go tonight - *tonight*! It is so like that ghostly night when we buried the young child of Innocence; the same moon, the same three pale stars - and thou, O Devil!"

"Ah, well! isn't it better that she should forget?"

"Forget! *Forget* that she murdered the child of Innocence?"

"For a time only," I said.

"O Devil, if thou - but see! she is coming; she has followed me! She will chide me for remembering. She will curse me for my 'one atom of faith!'"

"Fear not, Soul," said I.

"Soul, Soul, why art thou here?" the woman asked of the tortured thing that lay prone upon the grave of her young Womanhood.

"Because - because I cannot forget the child of Innocence!" it wailed. "Go! go! Forget, if thou can'st - but curse me not!"

"I curse thee not, Soul. Come with me. I am unhappy with thee - but unhappier without thee!" the woman said.

And the Soul rose, and fell upon her neck and wept.

I remembered the day when the man-devil came to her from over the hills, in all the pomp and vain-glory of life.

He came like the materialization of a dream! She fell under the fascination of his steel-grey eyes, and became as one in a trance. He was bold and mystical and enchanting - and strong.

He came like a knight-errant of old, astride of a gaily caparisoned charger, and she held out her hands to him in welcome. He was arrogant and dauntless and kingly - and strong.

He came - like a prince from far principalities, his robe of Tyrian purple sweeping the ground. She received him with open arms, and gave him of her inheritance. He was brave and majestic and valiant - and strong.

He came like Apollo, his brow wreathed with Parnassian laurel. Her spirit met his spirit, and it was like the meeting of the waters. He was grand and beautiful and romantic - and strong.

He came like a "conquering hero," flushed with triumph, and heralded by the loud alarums of victory; and she fell on his neck and kissed him. He was resplendent and proud and stately - and strong.

He came like an "army with banners," treading to the strains of martial music; and she cast herself a virgin sacrifice on his altar fires. He was confident and wicked and cruel - and strong.

He came like a red, red Devil from Hell; and she fell down on her knees and worshiped him! He was hard and cynical and devilish - and strong.

"Show me the glittering paths of Wickedness," she said. "Lead me to the Crystal Palace, whose walls imprison rainbows! Bring me within the sound of those rare voices, dowered with a note to soothe lost souls in Hell!"

He said, "I will."

And he did; and in her delirium, her mad joy, she murdered this child of her Soul - this child of Innocence and Truth. Then she and her stricken Soul stole out in the night, and buried her dead - here in this lone, forsaken grave.

This lone, forsaken grave! whither no kindly feet, save those of her Soul, ever made a pilgrimage! This lone, forsaken grave! which knows no visitation, save that of her Soul, and the cold, unfeeling winds which sweep above its eternal silence!

The man-devil went on his way triumphant, as the bee that kisses the rose, remembering not the one among the many, whose fragrance he has sipped.

She waited for his returning, and arrayed herself as a bride for her bridegroom: but he came not.

She lamented and bewailed, refusing to be comforted; and went out and poured her tears into a rock's breast: still he came not.

She clothed herself in sackcloth and ashes, and gazed from her window far out over the sand and barrenness, as though watching for the passing of an angel: still he came not.

She reviled herself that she ever was born; cursed the father who begat her, and the mother who bore her, and blasphemed God: still he came not.

Years passed.

Others came and whispered in her ear that the paths to the Crystal Palace were just as alluring as ever, the rainbows just as entrancing, the music of the rare voices just as ravishing!

She followed them, but the palace was turned to pitch; the rainbows, to bands of mourning; and the melody of the rare voices to maddened discord!

A look of horror, terrible to see, overspread her face, as if she had seen a ghost.

I crept stealthily to her side and whispered:

"Let us go back to the lonely grave on the mountain side, and bury your Womanhood so deep that its ghost can never arise to haunt you again!"

She shuddered, but said, "I will."

"Tonight?" I asked.

"Ah, no; not tonight! The moon is full, the three pale stars are out - and my Soul is on watch."

"When - if not tonight?" I asked.

"When my Soul sleeps!" she whispered.

Yours yesterday, today, and forever!
THE DEVIL.

*

THE STORY OF LIZZIE MCGUIRE

by Herself

[Frank Corey Voorhies]

- 1902 -

To

My Great Snakes

I have decided to put down in my diary a full account of myself and my feelings, for I am queer.

I am queer, very queer. Some folks think I am nutty.

I am a sweet, dear maiden of thirty-five summers, and I have lived in Chelsea all my life. Surely, that is enough. I need not add, after telling that, that my parallel cannot be found on earth to-day.

Think of it. Thirty-five years and in Chelsea.

Pity me, Great Snakes, pity me.

My young heart is bursting its suspender buttons, and all because I have been confined to the barren wastes of my native burg.

No kind young man has ever suggested that he become my Great Snake.

No kind young man has ever suggested that he bear me off on horseback to a four-roomed flat and an oil stove.

I am convinced of this, and it has made me queer, almost bughouse.

I have a marvellous capacity for beefsteak and onions.

I am broad-gauged; and, if you do not believe me, have a look at my photograph on the fly page.

Unlike my predecessors, I am not a philosopher of any very pathetic school.

I am a philosopher of my own make, because, like others, I need the money.

Money is dirty stuff to handle; but I am willing to take a chance, as do the rest of you.

I care for neither good nor bad (money), if I can pass it on the electric cars.

I have what I call a NIT conscience.

I am not exactly daffy over the subject of myself, but still I do not mind saying that I am one of the best ever.

I have a bunch of friends in Chelsea, and I have looked them over pretty thoroughly. But in vain. I cannot find any one whom I can call my parallel. There are those of varying depths and widths, but they are not in my class. I trot in the two hundred and ninety pound class, and none of the villagers over our way can tip the scales at my figure. I have a depth and width all my own. The gang all pass me their gosh darned smiles because I am such a heavy husky maiden.

There are about forty or fifty of these confounded idiots.

I have dipped into literature in my endeavor to find my parallel, and the nearest I can come to it is in Katie Rooney who wrote "A Lovely Pair of Arms; or, How would you like to be the Iceman?"

Katie and I have lots of moods and feelings in common.

I often feel like Katie did when she penned those immortal lines, "Love is like a Dago. It comes up and hits you when you are not looking."

I see from those words that Kate had groped in darkness. Her fresh young soul pined for a realization of her dreams. Her heart had been pierced by all the heavy emotions of this cruel, black world.

Or she had dyspepsia. I am not sure which.

But I am a genius, and don't you forget it.

I do not dare to get too far from the subject of myself for any length of time for fear that you may mislay the fact that I am the whole thing.

I was born in Chelsea, Mass., in 1867; and, if the town does not live to shake hands with itself when I move, then Great Snakes deliver it.

All of my family were Irish.

So am I.

The only days in my life when the barrenness of Chelsea has seemed to brighten up and get a move on it has been the thirty St. Patrick Days that I can vividly recall.

My brother is a bar-tender, and my sister makes sandwiches for a lunch-counter in Boston.

There is no bond of any sort between me, Lizzie McGuire, and my brother and sister.

The only tie I can think of is a note of my brother's that I hold for sixty-three dollars.

Oh, how my little, thirty-five year old maiden heart yearns for recognition!

Oh, if my sister - she of my own flesh and blood - would come to me and understand me! If she would come and throw her arms around me, and let our sisterly love grow warm!

But she does not do it.

And, oh, if my brother would come to me and understand me! If he would come and say, "Here, Liz. Here is that sixty-three"!

But he does not do it.

Is it because I am the genius of the family? Or is it because I am easy?

I am beginning to think it is because Brother Bill is a genius.

July 2.

Among other things I have, in my own bright, little way, learned how to feed myself and enjoy myself during the process.

I am a rattling good feeder, with a capital "F."

It takes a genius to know how to eat; and my healthy, fat thirty-five years knows it all in the eating line, and don't you forget that.

I am now an A1 feeder, and can finish any old thing in the food line in short order.

My philosophy of eating is extremely easy and simple, and you need not be in the gray-haired forties or fifties to become one of my disciples.

The art of feeding revolves around two points: feed whenever you get the chance, and take as large bites as your mouth can hold, comfortably or otherwise.

In this way you can eat beef quickly, and get ahead of the rise in prices.

Down with the Beef Trust, I say; and the only way to down it is to eat fast and much.

There are those who eat and drink for the sake of eating and drinking. They are soubrettes.

But I have learned one particular art of which I am proud. It has strengthened my opinion that I am a genius.

I have learned how to eat a sausage.

I place two five-inch gray sausages on my plate before me. (In selecting sausages, always see that they are fitted with gray tights.)

I contemplate them.

They make me think at once of the Dog Show, where the dog biscuit and the brass collar are the emblems; of the bench show where lines of stalls flank the long hallways; of yelps such as only the hungry fox terrier can emit; of the pound where are held the mongrels of the city and of the doubtful butchers.

The mere sight of a sausage does tricks with my mind.

I poke the south-eastern corner of the sausage nearest me with my fork, and with my knife I jab it as nearly in the centre as possible. Then with my right hand, or paw, as my genius dictates that I say, I raise it to my lips and carefully insert it between my two rows of white store teeth (bought for $4.98 per set, with teeth extracted without pain, free of charge).

Gee! How happy I am when I chew that tender old sausage.

I think of the adorable lines of an old German poet: "Oh, vere, oh, vere, is my leedle dog gone? Oh, vere, oh, vere, can he be?"

"Ah! dear, old, indigestible *Seinerwurst*" I say, "what t'ell do I care if you do give me a pain across the middle? I am game, I am."

The half of sausage then slips down my little red lane and into my stomach, where it is greeted by the glad hand. My stomach is dead game, too, and would not let on to a sausage that it could not digest it. My stomach is the stomach of a genius, and there are only a few like us. Let me tell you. The philosophy of my stomach may be summed up in the words of itself, which are: "If Lizzie likes it, then I'll try my best."

You can see that my stomach is subservient to my palate, as all geniuses' stomachs should be.

My fork grabs another half of the beautiful, round gray sausage.

Oh! Such ecstasy!

And thus I push the remaining three pieces of sausage into my face; and, as the last half slides through my gullet, my character changes.

Have I eaten too fast or too much?

Neither, surely.

But, somehow or other, I have what common folks call a pain.

And a confounded painful pain, too.

My festive stomach lifts up a silent cuss word or two, directed toward Simms, the butcher.

There seems to be nothing doing in the digesting line in little Lizzie's stomach.

I put my feet on the mantel-piece. The entire world is now one great big sausage, and I feel that I am slowly slipping off it. My mind is capable of conceiving but one idea, that confounded sausage.

I know now, Great Snakes, where to find that damnation you have told me so much about.

All I have to do is to look at a sausage, and I get the cramps.

You can bet all that is coming to you that the fellow who said that life is a tragedy had eaten sausages before he said it.

As the years pass, I shall put away sausages under my belt; and after each good eat I shall, no doubt, have a good old-fashioned pain like mother used to have.

For this is the art of feeding.

And meanwhile give me the adorable gray sausage that the Beef Trust cannot touch.

Hurrah for sausages!

July 3.

Sometimes, when I wander out around this tired old village of Chelsea, I fall into a half-dazed, half-comatose condition, and my wonderful mind takes excursion trips to distant lands.

To-day it went to Revere Beach, at reduced rates.

There I saw the long, curved beach, with its pebbles, its sand, its tin cans, and its castaway lunch boxes. The adorable scent of roasting peanuts and popping corn was wafted against my delicate nostrils. The groaning, straining melody of a merry-go-round organ played ecstatically upon my sensitive ear-drums. There I heard the grinding rattle of the steeplechase horses, reminding me, and tearing my stout, thirty-five-year-old heart with the thought of the daring young man who has never suggested to me that

I fly away with him on horseback.

Oh, such a beautiful ocean, too!

How many Venuses have come out onto that beach! How many graceful fairies, with peroxide hair and pencilled goo-goos, have never dared to touch those beautiful, briny, busily babbling wavelets as they dash up in breakers six inches high! How many of these damsels of the chorus have feared to lave in that great, grand, glorious ocean, lest their bathing costumes might fade and their cheeks lose their rosy hue!

I stood on the beach, and took a look at that old ocean, dreaming sweet dreams.

But my dreams were shattered by an urchin who ran wildly from the waters, yelling, "Hully Gee! Dat's cold, dat water is."

I walked on a little way.

Then I stood still.

"This is the gateway to that fool-killer, the Loop," I muttered to myself. "I am a fool. Yes, frankness is one of the marks of my genius. I am a fool. So I will hie me in, spend my nickel, and loop the Loop."

I went up and bought a ticket, and entered the enclosure by a gate that was two sizes too small for one of my broad gauge.

Finally, I did, by hard pushing, manage to pop through the aperture; and, as I landed within, a smile, a heavenly, beauteous smile floated across my fair, cherry lips.

Oh, how I smiled!

In fact, I almost forgot my genius, and laughed outright.

And with good cause, too, because I had passed a bum quarter on the door-keeper.

Well, I and my sensitive nature decided to board a car, and take the flying trip.

To think that I, Lizzie McGuire, the genius from the sleepy town of Chelsea, should loop the Loop.

But I did.

The first thing I remember was a sensation similar to the one felt by passengers when an elevated train stops. It threw me back about two feet, all in a bunch, and I could hear the seat crack.

Then I started on my journey heavenward.

And then, oh, then!

I stood balanced between sky and earth and on the brink of the most entrancingly steep incline that you can imagine.

How my fat heart fluttered!

"Let her go!" I wimpered with my angel voice.

And the attendant gave me a shove and a start on my downward trip.

My heart turned a double somersault and landed on the back of my neck. My breath came and went in the proverbial short pants.

Down, down, down!

Gee! How I flew!

Such sensations!

Oh! Ah!

Ugh!

Wow!

Suddenly it seemed as though the track came up and slapped me in the face. A thousand little devils seemed to be pouring ice-water down my collar and along my backbone.

My knees flew up.

My head flew down.

They met.

Such a headache!

As I whirled over, with feet up and head down, I felt like a heavy-weight acrobat doing his turn over six elephants.

Where, oh, where, would I land?

I began to choose my pall-bearers.

When I reached the downward whirl of the confounded Loop, it seemed that my body was trying to get a lap or two ahead of my head.

It seemed as though four horses were trying to separate me from the lid of my brain.

The first thing I knew I was flying up another incline and around in circles. But by the time I reached the transfer station I was Lizzie McGuire again.

A little the worse for wear, perhaps, but still Liz, I left the Loop and walked out toward the beach.

Just as I left the gate, a handsome young man smiled at me, and then he followed me.

I turned and looked.

He smiled.

So did I.

He came close to me, and said, "Tell me, pretty maiden" -

Then I woke up and found myself wandering around alone on the streets of Chelsea.

That's my luck every time.

If I could have slept a few minutes longer!

Just to have met the nice young man.

Bang!!!

I awoke with a start this morning.

It was a flying start.

Young Patrick jumped into the glorious Fourth by setting off a cannon cracker in the front hall.

It shook my windows and it jolted me; and, forgetting my sedate manners and my two hundred and ninety pounds of womankind, I leaped from my downy couch with fear, and landed on a tray full of dishes that had been left from my supper last night.

Farewell, dishes and tray!

Smithereens!

I often rise early in the morning, and gaze out of my window at the barrenness of Chelsea.

But I do not always get out of bed on the bounce as I did this morning.

However, this morning, with the excitement caused by a cannon cracker and a tray full of broken crockery, I was unable to sleep more, so I put on my kimono and sat by the window to dream.

To-day is the day that the Americans freed this country for the use of the Irish, so you may see why my dreams took on a red, white, and blue hue.

I dreamed that the clock struck nine and there came a rap at my door.

I opened it, and there stood a young man.

My Great Snakes!

I bade him enter, and said, "Whatst wouldst thoust, Great Snakes?"

"It is you, Lizzie McGuire, that I am after," he said in a soft, melodious voice; "and I want you to put on your glad duds, and come with me. We will canoe on the river."

Oh, how my two-ninety did tremble.

"You cannot lose little Lizzie," quoth I.

And off we trolled to Riverside.

He had a lovely canoe.

But it lacked beam enough for me.

I am a very wide article; and, try as I would, I could not squeeze into that confounded canoe.

Finally, he found a larger one, and managed to tuck me in.

Then off we went.

There was a good crowd on the river, but we managed to reach midstream.

All at once we tipped.

"Trim boat, trim boat," he shouted.

I moved my foot two inches, and we regained our equilibrium.

We paddled along slowly, as my Great Snakes found me heavy freight.
I smiled.
I chatted.
I giggled.
I did everything that foolish, popular young girls do; but his face never brightened.
He began to perspire.
He began to heave.
"This paddle seems to weigh a ton," he said at length.
"Or, perhaps, it is you," he added, wiping the perspiration from his brow.
Men are so cranky.
Even my Great Snakes was a crank.
He worried me.
He made me perspire, too; and, as I reached to my belt for my kerchief, I must have moved some part of my bulky anatomy.
It was all done in a second.
Kerplunk!
The canoe went over in a jiffy.
And I went with it.
So did my Great Snakes.
"O Lord! O Lord! oh, help! oh, murder!" I murmured, keeping my head cool. "I'll sink! I'll drown!"
But I didn't.
The canoe sank; but little Liz floated like a cork, with her two hundred and ninety pounds' displacement.
The police boat was near, and they threw a life preserver to my young man.
They threw a strong rope to me, and preferred to take a chance at towing me rather than lift me to the deck.
They could not pull me very close to shore before I scraped, as I draw about six feet of water when I am afloat.
Then I got up, walked ashore and shook myself like a little Fido, until my Great Snakes, damp but game, came up to where I stood.
We found that we were in Norumbega Park; and he was ashamed to take me home, as we both looked like ducked rats.
So we sat in the sun, and dried.
When the moisture had evaporated, we started for a walk.
It was then I learned the make of my escort's trousers.
They were the kind that you can see in front of Salem Street stores.
"All this for three dollars."
They had shrunk, and were half-way up to his knees.

But still I was proud of my Adonis.

I have such a sensitive, impressionistic nature that even my ducking could not take the starch out of my ardor.

In my opinion, he was a bird.

We walked around to look at the animals.

We were not the only animals in the park.

As we stood before the monkey cage, my character changed.

I felt sure I saw young Pat Gilhooly hanging to the cage and shaking the wire screen.

He shook with a good old Irish temper, and all at once it gave way, and with a crash the whole cage, wire and all, came over on me.

Oh!

Then I woke up to find myself in Chelsea, barren, sleepy, dead Chelsea, and sputtering around me was a pack of popping fire-crackers that Pat had tossed into my bedroom.

I could hear his retreating footsteps in the hall.

The son-of-a-gun.

July 5.

I have in me the germs of a corking good prize-fighter.

If I were a man and could earn my living by fighting, you can gamble that the world would have to recognize me as an intense heavy-weight.

I have the personality, the nature of a Sullivan, a Corbett, a Jeffries, and a Sharkey.

But I am a poor, thirty-five-year-old female. I cannot fight, even though a good scrap means easy money - sixty per cent. to the winner and twenty per cent. to the loser of the gate receipts.

I have that tenacious, never-get-licked, scrappy disposition that makes prize-fighters of men.

Now I would like to be such a man as is Jimmie Flaherty, the "Coffee Cooler," of Salem, Mass.

I have met the gentleman once, while he was visiting the family of his sparring partner here in the sleepy barrenness of Chelsea.

I have twelve printed, pink-tinted pictures of Jimmie that I keep in the top tray of my old, canvas-backed trunk.

They were taken from the *Police Gazette*.

Often, late in the evening, while I am brewing a cup of tea in a kettle over the gas-jet in my room, I take these pictures from my trunk, and place them in graceful array along the edge of my washstand.

Then I gaze at them until my stout, thirty-five-year-old heart flutters like an aspen leaf before an electric fan.

I am certainly dead stuck on Jimmie Flaherty.

He is a regular Napoleon to me.

And he came very near to winning the Richard K. Fox belt. He did, so he did.

As I look at his photographs, I fall in love with him more and more.

The twelve pictures of him that I have are all alike, but so different.

In the first he is a strapping big fellow, posed as if for a cigarette picture. I fall in love with him.

In the second he stands with his left drawn high and his right drawn ready for an upper cut. I fall in love with him.

In the third he looks as though he could lick anything from Chelsea to Roxbury. I fall in love with him.

In the fourth his eyes are bright, as though he had them on the check he will receive from the management after the bout is over, whether he wins or loses. I fall in love with him - and the check.

In the fifth he looks like a lobster. I fall in love with him.

In the sixth he is greasy, and looks as though he needed the money. I fall in love with him just the same.

In the seventh he seems groggy, and I am sure a soft tap on the solar plexus would put him down and out. I fall in love with him.

In the eighth he looks sleepy, and the night before he no doubt spent in Chelsea. Still I fall in love with him.

In the ninth he reminds me of a butcher in a South Omaha packing-house. I fall in love with him.

In the tenth he seems as fresh as a conductor on the Winchester and Woburn electric cars. I fall in love with him.

In the eleventh he looks as though his wife had gone through his pockets the night before. I fall in love with him (and I hope his wife will not see this).

In the twelfth he is throwing out his chest and holding up his head as though he was afraid of spilling his load. He looks as though Baltimore could not turn out enough good old rye to fill his tank, and his chin is thrown out with the confidence of a man who never takes a chaser after downing a fifteen-cent drink. He seems about to say, "Any old sour mash. That's all." Oh, how vividly in love with him I fall!

I love a man who can hold his refreshments like a gentleman.

As I sit here with my feet on the gas-jet and gaze at the twelve *Police Gazette* pictures of Jimmie, I think that he is a lallapaloosa.

He reminds me of my Great Snakes.

He reminds me of the young man I have pictured who will come and take me home with him some day.

As I look out of the window and gaze at a tenement house and a cop who is asleep on his beat, I wonder, yes, I cogitate.

Will my Jimmie Flaherty ever come?

Some day, my Great Snakes, some day.

Damn it!

July 6.

I have said that I am alone in this world.

I have made an error, as I am not quite alone.

I have one hanger-on that I cannot lose, and she manages to keep herself around my vicinity most of the time.

She is the lady who does my washing, and I call her my "laundry lady."

I sometimes call her my ammonia lady, as she uses some sort of a chemical in the water when she does my clothes up. It coaxes holes in white goods, I know that.

Anyway, she is as different from me as day is from night. She believes in hanging around a person who owes her two dollars for washing, and she believes in jollying the reticent ones until they come up with the mazuma.

My beliefs are along the lines of an entirely different creed. If a person owes me money, and I cannot get it for the asking, well, give me an axe. I'll take it from them by violent separation.

Even if I have to use a gun.

But my laundry lady is all to the good.

She taught me all I know about how to do up starched clothes.

But she cannot extract money from me unless she gives me gas.

I am odd and a genius, and I never pay bills.

I am a thief, too.

My father was a second-story man, so I guess. I come by my propensity for pinching things in a perfectly natural way.

I am not wealthy enough to be called a kleptomaniac. Still there is some spirit hanging about me that makes me love to annex things, as Dan Daly would say.

I shall never forget how I swiped three dollars from the lobster that lives in the flat just below us.

You see the old man I refer to is a veteran of the Spanish War, and he draws a pension.

One of his legs is shorter than the other because it was broken in the war, and had a bum set.

He broke it while running away from a skirmish.

Somehow he managed to get the pension, but the pension officers did not know which way he was running when he received the fracture.

The old war-horse loves his liquor, but hates to go out and get it.

He has the Chelsea spirit, and it pains him to move around much.

One day he called me down to his flat, and I went. "What can I do for you, my dear Alphonse?" I said with my usual happy smile and sunny look.

"Liz," he said in his kind old way, casting a squinting look at my thirty-five years and two hundred and ninety pounds of womankind, "Liz, I want you to get me a gallon of good old Bourbon. As I know your fair young palate is that of a genius and a connoisseur, I intrust these four bones of the republic to your chubby hand; and, if you will hie yourself into the city of Boston and exchange them for four quarts of the 'best made,' you will do your dear Alphonse a great favor."

Thereupon he thrust into my lunch-grappler four crisp one-dollar green boys.

I put on my gray crepe de chine, and took the next car for the big burg.

My wonderful mind was in deep cogitation meanwhile.

Here was my chance to rake off a seventy-five per cent. commission.

I am a thief and a wonder at figures.

When I reached town, I went straightway to my brother, the bar-keep.

I asked him the price of corn juice.

"De prices vary, Liz," he said. "Anywhere frum one samoleon ter six fer a gallon."

"How about the dollar stuff?" quoth I.

"Well," said he, "them's fair goods, them's fair goods. Them's der kind we serves ter cabbies and waiters at 10 cents per throw. But what do youse want wid hilarious liquids? Youse are not hitting it up, are youse, Liz ?"

Oh, how the language of brother Bill does rile me!

And how I do think of that sixty-three whenever I see him.

If I could only get my hands on that chunk of dough that I so foolishly let slip from my pocket-book!

What would my laundry lady say if I did get it?

She would quote Kip, and spout, "Pay! Pay! Pay!" I suppose.

Anyway, I got him to pour me out a gallon of one-dollar fire-water, and then he pasted an Old Crow label on the demijohn at my suggestion.

I took the stuff to the old vet, and he smacked his lips as he let it slide down his red gullet. He said he always did like Old Crow.

"Where ignorance is bliss, 'tis folly to be wise."

But I am wise to the fact that little Lizzie has three one-dollar bills tucked away in her purse; and, when the vet and I drank to the health of

the pension office, I sighed,
"After you, my dear Alphonse."

July 7.

I have never told you about the joint where I hang out.

In this flat where I drag out this accursed, gosh-hanged, gol-darned existence of mine, there lives a family whose uncouth ways and primeval manners grate upon my sensitive, genius nerves.

I have two rooms, with stove heat, oil light, and the free use of the family bath-room in this flat, for which I hand out six juicy dollars per week.

Oh, how I do weary of the Nothingness!

If a young man who would be my Great Snake should knock at my parlor door right now and offer to take me unto his heart, I would say, "In a minute," so quickly that he would develop heart disease.

But I was talking of my rooms and our flat, and I must not let my mind wander to love, sweet love.

As I said, I have free use of our bath-room; and I hate to enter the dreariness of the place.

Mr. and Mrs. Gilhooly, from whom I rent my rooms, and the three little Gilhoolys persist in using the bath-room as a depository for their foot-wear.

I can stand tooth-brushes, but deliver me from shoes.

Shoes! Shoes! Shoes!

Oh, the dreariness and the wofulness of the Nothingness in this barrenness and sleepiness of a Chelsea bath-room!

I have been told that one of the horrors of the Inquisition, in which the pinnacle of cruelty was reached and perched, was the forcing of victims to read newspapers that were filled with cheap patent medicine advertisements.

Well, this punishment was not one, two, three as horrible as it is, compared to the tortuous spasms that run up my vertebra whenever I see those shoes in our bath-room.

My very pathetic philosophy cannot stand for a line of broken-out, rundown shoes that extends half-way around a dingy bath-room.

There are, in the bunch, three ancient Congress boots that belong to the old man Gilhooly. The side elastics are has-beens and merely suggestions of their former worthiness.

The sides of each shoe are, I should judge, eight inches apart; and the entrance apertures are big enough to admit a ton of coal without being touched.

Old Gilhooly could put them on the floor, take a run, and jump into them without touching anything but the soles.

They are what one would call seven-masters, and they do jolt my artistic nature muchly.

I said above that there were three boots.

These are the remnants of two pairs.

Mrs. Gilhooly used the other shoe for a flower-pot; and it now hangs, beautifully gilded, before the dining-room window, containing a blooming sweet potato, with a weeping willow effect.

I do not blame it for weeping. It brings tears to my own crafty eyes.

Next in the line come a pair of high button boots, with but few buttons left, a pair of $1.98 Oxfords, and two pairs of cracked, patched, dilapidated, passé, once-upon-a-time, out-in-front, out-in-back, out-on-the-sides, high-heeled slippers.

This display belongs to the exhibit of Mrs. Gilhooly; and, as I gaze at them backed up against the bath-room wall, it sets my odd, philosophic mind to work, and I think great thoughts.

Such thoughts as will bring me fame.

Such thoughts as will make my name and my writings the watchwords of future generations.

I think, "Such a sloppy weather!"

Following Mommer Gilhooly's footwear come two pairs of muddy, laceless hoof coverings of a smaller size. These belong to young Patrick Gilhooly, and the sight of them makes my thirty-five years of womankind tremble with contempt.

I have the natural aversion to a small boy that is part of the make-up of every maiden of thirty-five, and in Patrick we have the essence of the mischievous, red-headed Irish kid.

His hair is as bright a crimson as the sunsets in cheap tea chromos.

His face is hidden behind a screen of freckles.

To see him once is to remember him always; and, as I see those shoes, I can imagine Pat in them.

So vivid is my imagination that yesterday I pictured him so completely in his boots that I involuntarily grabbed a poker that was lying on the coal in the bath-tub.

The remainder of the shoe line is made up of odd, ramshackle pedal cases that have seen better days many years ago.

Oh, how the gray matter of my mind is pounded and mauled by the sight of that shoe line!

Why am I so fussy?

It is because I am so odd.

And I am odd because it pays.

I need the money, and I am frank enough to say so.

But those shoes!

Gee!

The hamlet of Chelsea presents a nifty field to a student of humanity and human nature. Such a mixed bunch of gazabes are presented by no other town in the United States, I will gamble on that.

Think over all the places you know, such as Butte, Omaha, Saugus, and other big cities, and you cannot find such a motley group of burghers as Chelsea turns out.

We have a spicy conglomeration of Irish, Germans, Africans, Spiritualists, Christian Scientists, and Card Readers.

We have all sorts and conditions of men; and, as I am an old residenter, I am on to them all.

How weary I am of the Vacuity of it all. (That is another good word I have registered to my credit.)

Now I have the corner room of the corner flat in a corner tenement house, and there is not much doing on the streets that butt up to the building that I am not on to.

I will describe some of my neighbors.

There is an Irishman who lives with his family of eight healthy sons, and the old Shamrock is a roustabout for fair.

He drives a brewery wagon, and I guess he must get paid on Friday nights.

I can vouch for the fact that he never gets to work on Saturdays.

As he rolls into the street Friday evenings, it would appear that he had made his last delivery of bottled goods down his own red gullet.

He walks like a sea serpent and sings like a steam Calliope.

One can hear "Comb back to Erin" for four blocks on every Friday night if he will come out our way about nine o'clock.

Then there is a German who lives on the next street. He walks around the block for exercise six times each clear evening.

I should say he measured about six front feet by seven feet deep.

He looks like a young balloon.

All the small boys yell, as he passes, "Cut the guy ropes, Bill, and don't drop the parachute until you are at least four hundred high."

But he does not mind. Dutchy is immovable; and I guess he would smoke that pipe that looks like a golf club, even if the city was on fire.

I do not know any Africans, but a blind man in Chelsea can hardly help from seeing our colored population.

And the hundreds that I pass every day make my wonderful brain feel like a nutmeg on a grater.

But where Chelsea shines is in her collection of freaks.

She has more Spiritualists, Christian Scientists, and Fortune Tellers to the square inch than any other berg on earth.

There is a woman in the flat above us who claims to be a spiritualistic medium.

Of course, she is a bluff like the rest of her gang; but she is dead wise, all right, all right.

She knows how to squeeze dimes out of easy marks by jollying them into the belief that she can talk with the ones who have cashed in their chips, and she is making easy money.

She got me into one of her soirees one night, and told me she could put me in communication with any old has-been that I could think of; and I told her I would like to talk with the late Katie Hooligan.

She looked Kate up in the directory, and found that her number was 4,711 Hades; but, somehow, she could not ring her up. I guess the wires were crossed.

There was nothing doing in the Kate line for me; and Kate owed me $2.80 when she left, too.

That is why I wanted to talk to her.

Then I know a woman who is a Christian Scientist.

She tells me she is a disciple of a certain Mane Waddy, the great mogul of the twentieth century, new-fangled fanaticism.

She says that this Waddy woman has written several books that tell why everything is nothing.

I guess Mrs. Waddy does her writing in Chelsea.

The C.S. woman that I know says that Mrs. Waddy is just completing a new book entitled "Follow me, and you will wear Diamonds, or, How I catch a Lobster."

The C.S. woman came to me last week and told me that nothing is. We only think we are. Pain is a cinch. We only think it is.

Such a foolishness!

And two days later she called on me, and asked me if I knew any good painless dentist in Boston.

Wouldn't that jar you?

As for our Card Readers, I know several by sight; but, as I think they are even worse fools than I, I cut them out.

We have all sorts of guys in this town, let me tell you.

Do you wonder that the barrenness of it all is wearing my two hundred and ninety pounds to a shadow?

(See frontispiece.)

There are several things in this world that make me dead sore.

Here I am, of womankind and thirty-five years, looking for a young man who will make me his own little spare-rib of two hundred and ninety pounds; but still I have some things in mind for which I entertain a decided antipathy. (Good word, that last, isn't it ?)

There are things that we see and bump against every day, and many of them jolt me terribly.

Often that wonderful mind of mine chants a litany of its own, and it goes something like this.

From Chelsea, from Roxbury, from Camden, N.J., from Council Bluffs, from Butte; Great Snakes, deliver me.

From little Fidos with twisted mainsprings, from bar-tenders who persist in putting cherries in dry Martinis, from girls who order chicken a la Maryland in winter; Great Snakes, deliver me.

From women who wear blue dresses, green veils, and high-heeled slippers on the streets, from car conductors who wear diamond rings, from living pictures, women's orchestras, and the biograph; Great Snakes, deliver me.

From hotels that expect guests to pay their waiters, from postal cards, from letters written in lead pencil; Great Snakes, deliver me.

From house-breakers that work while you sleep; Great Snakes, deliver me.

From the man who employs a stenographer with hair of a different color than his wife's, from water cart drivers; Great Snakes, deliver me.

From the books of William Shakespeare and Nick Carter, from the woman who takes her dog on shopping trips, from cucumbers and milk; Great Snakes, deliver me.

From baked beans, brown bread, and Boston blue blood, from swell palaces built in dumps, from transplanted castles; Great Snakes, deliver me.

From young men who rubber on rainy days, from street organs that play "The Maiden's Prayer"; Great Snakes, deliver me.

From henpecked husbands, from the Elevated Road, from 10, 20, and 30 cent melodramas; Great Snakes, deliver me.

From faked prize fights, from swelled-head State senators, from gossiping women who get you in trouble "for your own good"; Great Snakes, deliver me.

From men and women who smell of sen-sen, from club women who know it all; Great Snakes, deliver me.

And so on and on and on, on, on.

But I would stand for all these things willingly if I could have the one great wish of the present moment gratified.

I wish I had a glass of beer, some potato salad, and a hot Frankfurter.

Give me these, and I will sit at continuous shows all day, and enjoy myself.

I was just now reciting this litany of mine when Pat Gilhooly, the pride of the household, came bouncing into my boudoir, and told me that his mother had just received a case of wet goods from Boston.

I could have embraced the child in my Happiness.

Patrick is too old to have any of his first teeth and too young to have any of his second teeth.

He smiled at me lovingly; and, as he parted his face, it seemed as though his features were trying to leave each other.

The upper and lower halves of his facial expression appeared to be trying hard to get a divorce from each other.

My heart would have gone out to the boy, were it not for the fact that I feared he would swallow it.

However, I went in, and quaffed the flowing bowl with Mrs. G.

It was fine.

I forgot all about the confounded litany.

July 10.

I find that I am nothing more nor less than a great big bluff.

"After the large show we give a grand stage concert in the main tent. Agents will now pass among you with tickets. Reserved seats, ten cents."

This is what we hear at the circus, and I feel that I am much on the order of the concert performers who bunco the reserved seat occupants.

As I look back over my diary and read what I have written, I can plainly see that I am a bluff, a fool, and a liar.

But there are others, and there is consolation in that.

I said I was a liar, but in reality I am only a fibber.

I have written a lot of fibs in my diary, and, like myself, it is all a bluff; but, if people go wild over young girls who seek notoriety by writing slush about themselves, why should I not make a stab at selling a few diaries?

I am looking for Happiness, and meanwhile I am looking for my share of the filthy lucre.

A thin, fine vapor of bluff hangs over me as I write; and it bids me choke off, as the people of to-day know when they have had enough.

I could be breezy, I suppose, and cover three hundred and twenty pages with "bluff and stuff," and then my diary would sell at bookstores for $1.10 net.

But what's the use?

I am too charitable to do that.

I have lived my thirty-five years buried in an environment that has differed greatly from the one I would have chosen, had I been able.

It has been my desire from childhood to be a ballet dancer.

Ballet dancers are bluffs, you know.

But I would not have to bluff.

The fact of the matter is that I am a little too big to be a coryphée. So, you see, I could not bluff with force.

I have enough "form" for three ballet dancers.

However, I never disclose my real self to the gaping crowds.

I decided long ago to devote my time to literature, because I know that my style and diction are without rivals in this country to-day.

What care I for the remarks of the people?

Have I not been told that my wonderful genius for writing is absolutely perfect?

Two of the greatest writers the world has ever seen have said so.

It happened that one of my essays entitled "Cause and Effect; or, Pie and Indigestion," was read at a spiritualistic conference when the spirits of Cicero, Catullus, and Virgil were present.

After it was finished, these three great German poets cried, "Bravo! Bravo! Lizzie is a genius! Such writings and word pictures!"

Then why should I do anything but write?

I am frank, very frank, and I say what I think.

I can truthfully say that I have never taken a bribe. Never have I taken a cent with the agreement that I would coincide with the views of others.

But I am trusting that my luck may change.

Offer me a dollar to say that black is white, and see how quickly I develop color-blindness.

Taking my cue from authors who have gone before, I will put down any words or collection of thoughts that my publishers think will sell.

You can bet your life on that!

What Lizzie Maguire is looking for is Fame with a capital "F."

Who can tell but that I may yet travel from city to city, and be wined, dined, and looked at as a freak, and I will carry my bluff along with me.

Oh, to be an author and a press agent, all rolled into one!

It would not only mean Fame, but Dough; and I am frank enough to say that that is what little Lizzie is out for.

My predecessors have left that confession out of their diaries.

But it is a ten to one shot that they have all had their pocket-books receivingly open, as they craftily laughed up their sleeves.

In laying bare myself and my genius, I hope I have not produced a wrong impression on your mind.

I have said that I am thirty-five.

But I have also said that I am a liar, so I may be forty-five.

I have explained that I consisted of two hundred and ninety pounds of womankind.

You can verify that by looking at the picture on the front page of this book.

I have said I am a thief.

But I am a liar, so I may be a Sunday-school teacher for all you know.

If I were all the things I have said I am, would you, kind reader, put much faith in me and my words and my book?

Not on your tintype!

It takes narrow-minded persons to think that the great American public is sufficiently narrow-minded to take them seriously when they make a bluff that they are stars and self-discovered geniuses, just because they sling a pint or two of ink on a few white pages.

Great Snakes, deliver me!!!!

*

THE STORY OF WILLIE COMPLAIN

by Himself

[Robert James Shores]

- 1902 -

PREFACE

A short time ago there was given to the world a Portrayal. It was the product of the brain of a geniusess, living in Butte, Montana. At that time few people had any suspicions that there was another such genius wasting away in the same vicinity. By a marvelous stroke of good fortune the author has secured the manuscript of this other Portrayal. It resembles, in some respects, the one first published, but it can easily be seen that it is the outpouring of another personality.

The name of this first Portrayal has been on everyone's tongue, - and, I have been informed, will soon be on cigar boxes. This being so, it may interest the public to read the Story of Willie Complain.

Robert J. Shores

Butte, Montana.
January 13, 1902.

I, of mankind and indefinite years, will now set down as full, if not as frank, a Portrayal as I am able of myself, Willie Complain, for whom the world contains but one parallel.

I, too, am odd. Doubtless I am the oddest of all oddities, for I was born to excel. If I had been born a bee, I should have been the queen bee; if I had been born cattle, I should have been the bell cow; if a beast, I should have been a lion; but being born a man, I am odd - and an Imitation.

Greatness, like genius, is merely comparative. Doubtless you will say that Mark Twain is a humorist, but I am, oh, much more clever. If he is funny, I am funnier. If he is great, I am greater. Where he is witty, I am a wit. Oh, the utter emptiness of everything but me!

I am an Imitation.

Perhaps you are inclined to doubt this?

Well, to be frank, I doubt it myself, for, you see, I am incredulous; most sublimely, gloriously, wonderfully incredulous.

It is a gift.

And an affliction.

Being, as I say, of a doubtful disposition (or perhaps I should say doubting), I find it extremely difficult to believe in myself.

Is it not pathetic, - wonderfully, ludicrously pathetic?

On almost any old line I have come to the place where the earth meets the horizon. Standing there where the blue dome of heaven curves upward, I long to scramble up the sides of it. But I cannot, because I was not born a fly.

I shall spare you the harrowing details of my wonderful history. I do not remember much that happened during the first few weeks of my life. Doubtless this is due to the inability of my infant mind to grasp at concrete things, rather than any lack of effort on the part of my parents to instruct me.

I was born at Minneapolis, some time before the Chicago Fair. Whether Minneapolis will yet live to blush for this, I am not prepared to say. Neither do I care a damn!

You see I am reckless.

Fortunately for me, my father did not die. Otherwise I should not have been looking so well-fed to-day.

Apart from giving me everything I asked for, and some things that I did not ask for, he has given me nothing.

Yet I must confess, shameful though it may be, I am glad he is alive.

When I think that I might have been born in a polyandrous country, and so had several fathers, I feel defrauded.

I gracefully retired from the high school with these things: - a very good opinion of myself; indifferent geometry and other mathematics; doubtful Latin; a broad conception of history and literature; paralytic philosophy that is not all my own; a taste for good tobacco; a well-fed soul, and a most excellent gizzard.

Right here is another thing about me, for while most people have livers, very few are possessed of gizzards.

With this equipment I struggled through two years at college, and now I am waiting.

I asked for bread, and I was given a stone. Which, as you may suppose, agreed exceedingly well with my gizzard.

I have a great deal to occupy my mind, but I do not permit it to do so. No one can be a true genius and philosopher of the paralytic school with an occupied mind.

Moreover, I am an Imitation, and I must follow the example of my original.

My life is not exactly a soulful one, but it suffices - I rise in the morning, eat three meals, work a little, write a little, smoke a little, and go to bed.

And I have a horror of toothpicks!

January 14.

If the world could but realize the full workings of my versatile mind, it would stagger it. J.P. Morgan would be confounded, the Steel Trust would cease to declare dividends, Russell Sage would give away his wealth, William J. Bryan would be stricken dumb, Butte would declare for temperance, Mary MacLane would forget to swear, and I - I should be in Warm Springs.

Poor little Willie Complain, how many people might you not do? But alone, held off, lost in the shuffle - poor little Willie Complain!

Had I been born a billionaire, I would by now have had my escapades in Town Topics. But I am not a billionaire, and God or Fate, or whosoever it was, has peeled from me my crust and thrust me into the world's waste-basket. Has left me a lonely, damned thing, with a desire for notoriety.

I am a paralytic philosopher awakening, and upon awakening, I cry out for someone to knock me on the head.

There is a pain that goes with these things when one is a genius and an Imitation.

I am filled with unrest.

I wish to give the world a negligee Betrayal of Willie Complain, his paralytic philosophy, his horror of toothpicks, his taste for good tobacco, and his excellent gizzard.

I wish to go out in the market place and exhibit my soul - en deshabille!

I wish to acquire that expensive, sought for, vulgar thing, - notoriety.

I wish to leave my poverty, my obscurity, and my horror of toothpicks, behind me forever.

I am bored to death with myself, and no wonder.

I wish to take this Betrayal to the very top of that loop-the-loop called "the world."

I wish to shove it off and watch it circulate.

Can I drag out my existence in this uncouth Montana town?

I, a genius, a philosopher, and an Imitation?

I see the picture plainly. Oh, good Angel, deliver me from it!

Surely, in this world of electricity, there must be one small bulb that shines for me alone. Some sixteen candle-power, to light me on my weary way.

If I did not hope for this, I should blow out the gas.

January 15.

So then, yes, I find myself at this stage of mankind and indefinite years - an Imitation; a fool, more or less; a philosopher of' the paralytic school; an indifferent liar; and, I own it with shame, no thief at all.

Even this aggregation of most dazzling attributes fails to satisfy me. But it serves to occupy my 18-carat mind, and keeps me from wondering what my good Angel has in store for me.

A philosopher of that paralytic school which is not all my own - hour after hour I sit in the back yard and contemplate the ash-heap.

It is not an unusual ash-heap. It is large at the bottom, and tapers at the top like a dish of circus ice-cream; but to me it is wonderful. For you see, I too, am wonderful, and to the extraordinary all things are extraordinary.

And as I sit there, to my versatile brain comes the thought, "Ashes to ashes; dust to dust."

Is not that remarkably clever of me?

I see an ash-heap, and it occurs to me, "Ashes to ashes; dust to dust."

So this back yard and the ash-heap forms the setting for the personality of me.

January 16.

I feel about six months of age.

Yet I know my feeling is not the feeling of six months.

These are the feelings of indefinite years.

The atmosphere of the outside world becomes quite oppressive, so I go out to my back yard and my ash-heap.

It is not clean nor sweet-smelling. It is delightfully like a pig-pen. I sit for hours beside an empty can. It is not even a pate de foie gras can; it is a lobster can. But it is well enough when you consider the ash-heap. It is, in fact, peculiarly fitting.

And I am congenial to all three of them, the back yard, the ash-heap, and the empty lobster can.

It is good to be congenial with something, if it is only the abandoned abode of a dead lobster.

What should I do if the back yard were a dish of strawberries and the ash-heap were whipped cream!

I feel about six months of age.

I repeat that I know my feeling is not the feeling of six months. For an infant of six months, even a philosophic infant is capable of little or no sensation.

The ash-heap reminds me of the dry, warped people of Butte. I know that the people of Butte are dry, because they are eternally irrigating their systems.

It is a source of satisfaction to me to contemplate the dryness of the people of Butte - it conjures up visions of long thin glasses and clinking ice.

But my Angel is sad, and being of a sympathetic nature, I weep also.

It may be that if I were the original, and not merely an Imitation, I should long for sterner things. It may be that I should find this occupation insipid and crave the cheerful surroundings of a graveyard.

Perchance, being a genius, I should take an unholy joy in butting into cemeteries, and sticking my gum-wads on the worm-eaten head stones.

But I am only poor little Willie Complain, and an Imitation.

I feel about six months old.

January 18.

I await the coming of my good Angel, and my horror of toothpicks becomes almost unendurable.

Meanwhile - as I wait - my versatile brain occupies itself with its fantastic philosophy, and I become calm.

The good Angel has given me some nice things. She has given me, among other things, my most excellent gizzard, of which I am passionately fond.

If you have the time or inclination, you can send me a two-cent stamp, and I will forward a chart of this most excellent gizzard. It is a Willie Complain gizzard of most perfect proportions.

Other young men and women have good bodies, some are even possessed of paralytic philosophy, but few have a gizzard. And those few, I am convinced, have never grasped the poetry of their internal machinery. They have not learned to scan the sinuous winding of their inner arrangements.

Some days, in the dampness of June, I have sat for hours in the back yard.

The greyness of the clouds, the wetness of the unceasing drivel, have entered into my veins. For of all things, drivel is to me most pleasing.

At such a time my body radiates with joy.

My blue blood flows quickly through my arteries.

My ribs grind together in an ecstasy of satisfaction.

My erratic and somewhat purplish stomach rests in calm content.

My lungs, feeling the freshness of the shower-bath, expand benevolently.

My heart works overtime, and whistles like a merry youth.

And my most excellent gizzard sings snatches of a rag-time ditty.

"It is good," I think to myself, "it is good to be alive." It is miraculously good to be a man young in the fullness of indefinite years. It is unspeakably heavenly to sit in the rain and contemplate my ash-heap.

So I sit and I cross my legs comfortably, and the water trickles joyously down into my boots.

There is a wonderful, lazy, unthinkable sensuality in a young man sitting in the rain.

A woman might sit in the yard. But she would wear rubbers probably, or sneeze at the thought of wet feet.

All is peace - and mud. But it is not peace that I want. Peace will come to me when I am older, and my neighbors will attend to the mud.

I am waiting the coming of my Angel.

There will be days of hail, and days of sunshine; but always there will be the dull grey line of the top board on the fence.

Imagine a life full of nothing more inspiring than ash-heaps and tomato cans. Imagine such a life tied in knots, stretched to the breaking-point, mauled mercilessly, and a cruel world playing Ping Pong with my tortured soul!

And with all this there is the grey line of the top board on the fence.

Oh, Angel, Fate, World, - some one bring me the top rail of my fence!

Bring it to me, full of slivers, intensely rough, intensely hard, and punctuated with angelic knot-holes.

Bring me this, and I ask for no more. One hour of this bliss and I shall be content the rest of my existence picking out the slivers.

I am rather fond of slivers.

But, oh, I loath toothpicks.

January 21.

There are three kinds of misery, and all are transitory, but each one seems more than infinite.

There is that misery which comes from a cold in the head and a lack of handkerchiefs.

There is the misery which comes of a hard bed and a desire to rest.

There is the misery which comes of a desire for something, and an ignorance of what that something is.

This is the misery which I, Willie Complain, am doomed to suffer.

Being as I am a philosopher of the paralytic school, I can sometimes bear up under my burden. When I feel the load growing too heavy for my young shoulders, I retire to the seclusion of the butler's pantry. There, surrounded by the tea urns, and gazing at my ancient horror - the toothpicks - I reflect upon my lot. I long, oh, how I long, to be real!

Must I bear always this feeling of insincerity and artificiality?

Oh, good Angel, come take me on your knee and shake my rattle. Come bring me peace and make me really live.

I am weary, weary, waiting.

After all nothing counts. If I desire to abuse my neighbor, shall I not do so? For, as love justifies itself, so does hate also, and if I see my enemy approach, it is my birthright to hit him with a brick.

But a world full of fools will never learn this. And since I realize they will not learn, I shall not run the risk of trying to teach them.

They can go to hell!

Oh, damn ad infinitum!

January 22.

It is night.

Night in the great city, night on the country downs. In fact, night everywhere in the immediate vicinity. And, being night, it behooveth me to rest.

But I rest not, nor shall I give you any chance to rest, either, dear reader.

After gracefully eating a half pint of salted almonds, with my feet on the bureau - always with my feet on the bureau - I am ruminating.

The world is made up chiefly of negatives and positives. You probably do not realize this, but you are neither a genius nor a paralytic philosopher.

So I repeat, in my rare egotism, the world is made up chiefly of positives and negatives.

What is the sky?

Not paper, at any rate.

What, is the wind?

Damned disagreeable.

What is fame?

Respectable notoriety.

What is my heart?

The pump-house of my system.

What is my soul?

A damnably harassed, tortured pretense.

What do we know?

More than we are at liberty to tell.

What are we?

The Original and the Imitation.

Of what good is the progress of the ages? Our science has not instructed us so that we can conjugate the "all-why." Science does not teach us why the robin prefers the fat worm to juicy beefsteak from Omaha and green young onions from California. Science has not told us why the moon persists in standing in the sky, night after night, instead of perching on the city hall. Science has not taught us why the mountains live on, year after year. Or even that they do live.

Being sublimely, immeasurably, delightfully, uniquely skeptical, I doubt that the mountains do live.

A very few centuries ago there were no handkerchiefs. Now we have handkerchiefs, and still have colds in our heads. We still cry out, and kick and struggle as the people did when they had no handkerchiefs.

Oh, the utter emptiness of everything but me!

I have walked in the summer by a little pond filled with lilies and surrounded by toadstools. The lilies, or toad-stools, or something, had a most highly-colored, tangible, vivid perfume. The sort of smell that makes one wish to grovel and poke one's nose in about the weeds.

You may shout and cry, you may struggle, kick and scream, if you are so undignified, but in your moments of calmness sometimes there will come back to you the fragrance of a swamp filled with lilies and surrounded by toad stools.

It is thoroughly entrancing.

What is its Hidden message? What secret would it whisper?

Why does the pond freeze when the weather is below freezing point?

Why does it thaw again and become a voluptuous sheet of water in the spring - to torture the spiral souls of the wretched onlookers'

We are but little wiser than when Omar hit the pipe.

The world is a pond filled with things damnably undamned, beautifully ugly, pink clucks, yellow fevers, human eyes, fifty-seven varieties of Heinz's pickles - and doggerel.

Oh, my good Angel, give me three days of golden happiness, in which I can shock my neighbors and be devilish, and then I will return to the fold.

Again, I say, the world is composed chiefly of negatives and positives.

Where are our pillows?

I am startlingly similar. I am delightfully tiresome. I am charmingly vulgar.
I am piquantly tragic - the while I may be smiling in my sleeve - and a sure
enough Devil.

I talk to a room full of well-bred people and compel their interest, ad-
monition and astonishment. As I have said, I am only an Imitation genius,
but I have a magnetic soul. I am not bow-legged, not hump-backed. When
I choose to talk in my own erratic style, adding a little truth to the lies and
nonsense, I have a noticeable way with me, a pose.

If one is possessed of no common sense, or average intelligence, it is well
to acquire a pose. I do not often put myself out to bore people to extinc-
tion. Being, as they are, of the genus fool, they cannot truly appreciate my
own utter idiocy.

Moreover, when a thing becomes too interesting it is often atrocious. In
fact, I may say it is pretty sure to be atrocious. Then, too, it may be infini-
tesimally destructive.

My conversation always hovers gently about my own charming personality, an interesting person - Willie Complain.

Pray, do not blame me for my ridiculous egotism. I am but an imitation,
and it is my duty to reflect. I am the moon, and my original is the sun.

This being so, I am a genius. I am deep in some things, and deeper in
others. I know things, I do not know that I know them, and I do not know
that I do not know them, which is tommyrot.

It is wonderful that I have gotten so far and not been up before the
Commission for the Insane.

Often I take this fact between the nut-crackers and crunch it slowly,
listening to the gentle cracking of it.

And every day it gets more nutty than the day before.

So I squeeze, and squeeze, and eat the nut, and try to be brilliant.

Yes, you may gaze at the chart which I will send for two cents. It is the
gizzard of an Imitation genius, a philosopher of the paralytic school.

And I shall tell you more about this gizzard, I think, before I have done.

One of the strongest things about me is my long memory. If it came to an
actual showdown I could, undoubtedly, put Methuselah out of business in
the memory line.

My mind has stored away everything that has happened since the day

I was born, and a good many things that did not happen. Probably, in the course of time, I shall be able to recall things that happened before I was born.

When I was a child I used to go out into the fields and lay on my back amid the toads and other vermin. I found them most congenial company. Hour after hour I would lie there gazing into the sky while the reptiles crawled gently, affectionately, over me.

Was it not weirdly, damnably pathetic?

At that time I was a young barbarian - but outwardly dirty and inwardly clean. Now it is vice versa.

And as I think of the little barbarian, the tide of tears rises within me until I tremble lest it pass the high-water mark. I shake with hard, dry sobs. They are much more piteous and effective than soft, wet ones.

My little sunburned hand reached out, but there was nothing for it. If there had been, I too, might have written with pride, "I am a thief."

But there was nothing.

Oh, the gloriously, pathetically, tragically enacted Nothing.

Oh, the utter emptiness of everything but me!

January 26.

There is something about house-tops that fascinates me. This is a sign of genius, and philosophy of the paralytic school.

So I sit gazing out on the house-tops.

As I sit thus, my versatile mind is at work to find new flaws in the rest of mankind.

Three doors to the right, left, or straight ahead it is the same. They all have chimneys and shingles. Oh, the wearisomeness of chimneys! The hypocrisy of house-tops!

And beneath the house-tops dwell those who are united in the bond of matrimony. These are the people who have sworn to love one another; but I, in my superior wisdom, know that they do not. And it occurs to me that not two out of a hundred of these have a shred of decency with which to clothe themselves.

True, I am not over-virtuous myself, but that does not excuse these others - for they are not geniuses. They are, as people go, virtuous. Therefore, they disgust me.

Being, as I am, a philosopher of the paralytic school, I have no patience with virtue.

Toothpicks are virtuous, and, oh, I have a horror of toothpicks!

Would it not be enormously better if the marriage ceremony were done away with? For then there would be nothing but love. Love is not given to all. I mean the Bohemian love of the genius. It is the love of a hen.

I look out over the house-tops, and I have a weary, disgusted feeling.

This is not a diary. Neither is it the autobiography of lunatic, as you might suppose. It is the catalogue of my peculiar, but wholly charming personality.

I am taking the temperature of my opaque soul and feeling its pulse. I am carefully scrutinizing the wall paper of my spirit. It is difficult to read, for it is shorthand.

The anguished unrest of my spiritual half-lights is disconcerting. For, while I have a perfect gizzard and an excellent liver, I am possessed of only half-lights.

This is a secret.

But why should I be ashamed of it?

Only last night I arose in the wee, sma' hours to quench my thirst. As I returned to my chamber I jostled against my soul, which was blindly groping in the passageway.

I said to myself, "I shall go mad."

But no, I shall not go mad, for I am an Imitation, and I was created mad.

When my Angel brings me my happiness I shall forget all this. All the little vertebrae of my spine will be drunk with joy.

My happiness will be of a most peculiar kind. It will turn handsprings, it will stand on its head, it will wag its ears, it will bray, it will sing, it will chew gum, it will trot, it will two-step, it will waltz, it will roll about in glee, it will snivel and wail, it will stand on its hind legs, it will squeak, it will yell, melt, blaze, chime, revel, carouse, swell, surge, advance, retreat, and do innumerable other stunts.

Words are comparatively useless things, and perhaps you will find the above rather confused. If not, you, too, are a genius, a philosopher of the paralytic school.

The nearest approach to happiness I have is eating.

Sometimes I go out into the butler's pantry and eat a salted almond.

First, I place the almond on my tongue and carefully lick off the salt.

Oh, the sublime rush of saliva that greets the salt!

Then I chew the nut carefully, gracefully, bringing exquisite pain to the tiny nerve of every molar.

And as it descends to my excellent gizzard, all my organs unite in a paean of ecstasy.

The world resolves itself into a salted almond, and I am the salt of the earth.

This is the art of eating.

Periodically I fall completely in love with my Angel.

She is so ethereal, so strong, so suggestive of pink tissue paper. Exactly the sort of being that my Imitation soul cries out for. I would like to hurl myself at her halo. I would love her, oh, passionately, prismatically, obliquely.

"What would you have me do, Willie. Complain?" my Angel would say.

"I would have you beat me, kick me, pull my ears, muss my hair, stick your fingers in my eyes," I would answer.

And about that time I will wake up.

Oh, damn, damn, damn!

Oh, the misery of Nothingness -

Oh, the utter emptiness of everything but me!

Oh, the wonderful, exquisitely bitter lonesomeness of Willie Complain!

Like the only grain of wheat in a mountainous pile of chaff, I am buried beneath the rubbish.

Like the tinkle of a cow-bell in a thunderstorm, my voice is drowned.

Like the only genius in a world of fools, I am deserted.

Oh, the timorous trill of a tropical twilight, the swooning silence of a midsummer moon!

My soul is an immeasurable moat of inventious intensity.

Oh, damn, damn, damn!

Damn everything and everybody!

Come to our bargain counter in profanity.

The latest things in curses given away at cost.

The world, the universe, be damned!

I have been looking over the confessions of a morphia-maniac. They are, to be sure, rather on the order of my Portrayal, but they are not nearly so wonderful.

For, what is insanity, induced by drug, compared to the divine disquietude of a paralytic genius?

What is the full-fraught fancy of a self-made lunatic to the diffusive diradiation of an Imitation imagination?

Through the infinitude of voiceless azure, the sublime sentiments of my glittering genius will dissipate the darkness of the dewless dawn.

The illumined inspiration of my sympathetic soul shall ravenously rend the dread domains of nimbused Nothingness.

And with it all the magnificent melody of the sovereign spheres shall brutally beat a devilish diapason of degraded damnation.

And I - I am suffering the inevitable enervation of lingering lunacy.

Oh, the utter emptiness of everything but me!

I am not high-minded. I am sensitive, sensuous, sensual, sinuous, similar, singular, sublime, superb, soulful, sorrowful, sympathetic - and all the other "s's" but sensible.

You see, I am a Philosopher with the philosophy of a cowherd.

Add nothing to nothing, and the sum is nothing.

Subtract nothing from nothing and the remainder is nothing.

Multiply nothing by nothing, and the result is nothing.

And so I go on, with my back yard and ash-pile.

February 7.

In this house where I magnanimously consent to live at the expense of my parents, downstairs, in the butler's pantry, there is a glass of toothpicks; sixteen wooden ones and one with an ivory handle.

The sight of these toothpicks, day in and day out, is one of the most frantically fanatical circumstances of my fool existence.

Every birthday I sweep out the pantry.

Ordinarily I am filled with joy at the prospect. I like the scratching of bread crumbs, and it always leaves my clothes covered with granulated grease stains. But the ominous obviousness of those seventeen toothpicks, calling attention to the instability of the human tooth - makes my soul peevish and my gizzard weep.

Now, more than ever, does the variegated vapidness of my execrating existence come upon me, when I fix my optics on those seventeen toothpicks.

During the inquisition a cultured cruelty was the pulling of the victim's teeth.

If the victim had been confronted day after day with this weary array of toothpicks, I think he would have rushed rapturously to the arms of that devilish dentist.

I am not undergoing an inquisition, nor am I the star boarder of a foolish factory. But I live in a house which affects me mostly through its toothpicks. I should like to cram them down the throat of the man who made them.

Dear me! It makes me so angry!

When I look at those seventeen toothpicks a pink flood of vexation ripples up and down my back.

Two heavy hands lay hold of my soul and tweak its nose mercilessly.

I should like to chase myself out of this house and hit the high places for anywhere.

Once I took the ivory toothpick out of the glass and wore it in my vest pocket for a day or two. I thought to diminish the apparentness of the other sixteen.

I put it back in the glass.

The absence of that one accentuated the somber solitude of the other sixteen.

Besides, the point penetrated my vest and pricked me in the ribs.

Often I lash myself into a frenzy and long to rush headlong from the butler's pantry. But I should return when hungry, so what is the use?

At such a time my life resolves itself into toothpicks, sixteen wooden ones and one with an ivory handle.

February 8.

Often I go into the library to flirt with death.

There is within me the latent spirit of Don Juan.

In the library there is an ink-well about a quarter of an inch deep, with black ink inside.

This ink-well completely fascinates me.

Sometimes I start to go out to my ash-heap, but I feel an irresistible impulse to go to the library and the black ink-well.

And here I flirt with death. The hole is narrow - only about an eighth of an inch across - but very black. I don't know whether it was intended for a soup tureen or a bath-tub, but I think it was meant to hold ink.

At any rate, it is full of Carter's writing fluid, and has a rare fascination for me.

There is something delightfully soothing for me in the blackness of that ink-well.

Some time, perhaps, I shall meet my death through it, but I shall have to swallow the contents, for the hole is so small I could not get my head in.

Death is wonderfully alluring to me.

"The silent sarcophagus might clasp within its close confines my mortal tenement, but my strenuous soul shall never be silenced while heaven re-sounds with the unwritten music of the spheres."

But first I shall await the coming of my Angel and my happiness.

And I am weary - weary waiting.

February 12.

I am in no small degree a sham -

I am, in fact, entirely an Imitation.

Possibly you may have wit enough to have grasped this already.

While all these vibrations of my soul are written in the utmost insincerity, they are more or less untruthful.

I don't know how to say this without leading you to believe that I am a liar.

These emotions are, however, very truthful for a sham - they are my life blood.

A thin vapor of originality hangs over me.

It is intangible, undefined, but none the less there. I cannot shake it off. I have lived the full sum of my indefinite years without disclosing the fabric of my soul.

That is, never to anyone but my Persimmon Pal. It may be that I have not heretofore mentioned this, my one friend. If so, it was an oversight. He is the man who used to clean our furnace. I think the thing that drew me to him first was the relationship he bore to my ash-heap.

I am an innate liar.

So then, yes, it is a difficult matter to show others that which they must have found perfectly apparent from the time they first opened this Portrayal.

But this is to be a complete Betrayal, therefore I shall write everything as I await my Angel's coming.

February 13.

Alas, I am no thief.

February 17.

To-day I followed the rainbow as far as my paralytic imagination would carry me. I stood on the hilltop and looked at the sea-pink valley beneath and the long stretch of what might be pineapple trees, but isn't. It put me in mind of my Angel, and the happiness she may one day bring me.

Some day my Angel will come and say, "Come with me."

And I will answer, "Yes."

And she will take me away to a place where it is dry and yellow - where the purple sunshine falls on the flirtatious hills and filmy, mosquito-netting clouds float by.

And the mountains shall skip like young rams.

And I shall be happy.

And the fruit of my happiness shall be young onions. Oh, vastly superior to the sort grown in California.

And my weariness shall shine as Sapolio.

"It is the last - the last of that Willie Complain," I shall say.

And the suffering public will rejoice.

And in the Pink Dusk I shall be saturated with even the joy of the Angel. And my soul shall rejoice as a porous plaster.

At times I go into the hallway and stand by the telephone.

Then it is that I believe in something. For a time this something is undefined and evasive, and then it resolves itself into something intensely tangible.

It is the telephone receiver.

I take the receiver and hold it to my ear. And then my soul is weary unto death, for Central is silent.

I cry out, and she answers nothing.

Oh, the agonizing nothingness of nothing!

Do you understand this?

Do you realize the awful tragedy of my young life?

My soul rushes wildly about seeking nothing, finding nothing.

And with all the pain and anguish, I cannot repress a smile.

For it reminds me of a newly-beheaded fowl.

Willie Complain - what are you, you desolate, wonderful, all-alone little being?

Why are you not of the maddening throng?

Why do you stand out dividedly against the horizon?

Is it that the maddening throng is somewhat particular about the company it keeps?

You thin, under-fed, little yellow dog; you youth-weary, philosophic little idiot?

Oh, the utter emptiness of everything but me!

To hell with everything!

Often, in the early evening, I hie me hence and go out into the Pink Dusk.

There is something about the Pink Dusk that makes me wish to lie on my back, kick my legs and yell in frantic joy.

In the Pink Dusk all is suggestive of chocolate creams. I have an intense feeling of spiritual stomach-ache.

Sometimes I think I am a peculiar article, not fit for Heaven, unappreciated on Earth, and not familiar enough with Hell to be at home there.

Every question is a query, and each why remains a wherefore.

I felt this in the Pink Dusk this evening, and the ceaseless pain it brought came to an end.

The Pink Dusk is not the Garden of Eden, nor the Streets of Cairo, nor a happy valley; it is the Pink Dusk.

Say this over to yourself six hundred and fifty times. Then, perhaps, you will get the idea.

The deep pink of the summer sky stirs me to a half-joyful pain. The deep purple of the sky gives my soul epileptic fits.

Oh, I could die, die, die!

But I shan't, for if I did, there would never be any more painful joys, or joyful pains.

The Pink Dusk can do no wrong.

Is not that an intelligent speech?

It is the speech of a philosopher of the paralytic school.

To-night a poem ran through my mind. It was peculiarly appropriate to my imitative genius. It was as follows:

*

The vision of accursed souls,
The birth of fire, death of day,
Nor fortune, fate, at all controls,
Nor priest explain away.

*

The dream of fools in Paradise,
The nightmare of the savage breast,
And terror with distended eyes
Attended on the rest!

*

This is a poem perfect. And it expresses most exactly the state of my mind. Oh, sweet Pink Dusk!

March 5.

Ever and anon I am seized with nearer, vivider sensations of love for my one friend, the Persimmon Pal.

He is so suggestive of my ash-heap.

I say to myself, "Why am I not a woman, that I may make him a good wife?"

But ever there is nothingness of nothing.

And ever there is the utter emptiness of everything but me!

There are quite a few things in this narrow world for which I, of mankind and indefinite years, have acquired an aversion. Or rather, it was created in me by the author.

My versatile brain sometimes chants this litany -

From persons who know things, and know that they know things; from the kind of woman who calls her form her "figure:" good Angel, deliver me!

From boors; from all other paralytic geniuses; from frauds; from self-conceit: good Angel, deliver me!

From union suits; from padded hips; from persons with singing stomachs; from literary novices: good Angel, deliver me!

From the soft, persistent fol-lol of disordered minds; from beefsteaks and onions: good Angel, deliver me!

From hip-garters; from cambric handkerchiefs in waists; from women who wear mustaches; from the kind of people who talk of legs at all: good Angel, deliver me!

From chewing gum; from imperceptible waist lines; from devil men: good Angel, deliver me!

From gently resting livers; from thieves; from bores: good Angel, deliver me!

From women on cigar boxes; from all other Betrayals; from a devilish young girl: good Angel, deliver me!

From vulgar language in books; from idiotic self-sufficiency; from supercilious poses: good Angel, deliver me!

And so on - and so on.

In these things I am sincere, and I think the public is with me there.

My genius is peculiarly a thing apart, and it cannot be described in words, except, perhaps, by the words, "Imitation Genius."

It is a thing that I have imbibed from others, though I was more or less a genius when born. Usually when anyone hears me make a commonplace remark, they see immediately that I am extraordinary.

For what is so extraordinary as the commonplace?

I have tried devotedly, aspiringly, to think that this backyard arid ash-heap are mine; but I know that they, too, are beyond me.

Compared with the picture of me and my ash-heap, the picture of Christ crucified with two thieves pales into insignificance.

It is ravishingly complete.

If I were a real, and not an Imitation, genius, I should be overjoyed at the picture of the Crucifixion. Not only at the art, but at the deed.

I know this is true, for I have a notable example of it.

And within me I feel that the picture of me and my ash-heap is infinitely superior.

Oh, dreariness, dreariness, dreariness!

Damn, damn, damn!

I feel to-day as though I should like to die.

Did I hear a voice say "Bravo?"

Tut! I am surprised that you should speak so to a philosopher of the paralytic school.

When I was six weeks old I grew unutterably tired of milk. And I said to myself, when I am six months of age they will give me beer.

But when I was six months old the beer was no nearer than before.

And again I said, "When I am a year old, surely the beer will come."

But it did not. And then I knew that it would never come.

For if one does not get beer when he is a year old, when will he get it?

And always there is nothingness.

Nothing is quite so nothingey as nothingness.

It is a hope postponed.

And my heart is sick within me.

It cries out, "Me to the apothecaries."

But I, being a genius, know that it will not find relief.

Why - why was I born?

Silly question, isn't it?

But that is the privilege of genius.

For it would be of no avail to be a genius if one had not the right to ask fool questions, expecting no answers.

I feel as though I should like to die to-day.

If it were the pain of pain alone that I had to bear, it would be a cinch.

But it is the pain of things that do not pain which makes the pain unendurable.

It is the sense of beautiful ugliness, and ugly beauty, and the sense of persimmons.

Name it, and you can have it.

It is this conglomeration of sensations that puts me out of business.

Why is a mouse when it spins?

This question haunts my brain. Hour after hour I say it over to myself, and the answer is no nearer. And always, there is the emptiness, the utter emptiness of everything but me!

Is thy servant a dog?

Was your good mother a cat?

Chaos! Confusion! Damnation!

Damnation! Confusion! Chaos!

I am not real. I do not seem real to myself.

I am an Imitation.

In such things my life is a white chip.

Sometimes I think of heroism.

And always it reminds me of that heroine who was so intensely heroic, so intensely feminine, that she sneaked in on her enemy and stabbed him in a bath-tub.

It is exalted; it is glorious.

What must be the delightful sc now?

I do not know what I should do.

Neither do I care a damn.

You see I am still reckless.

I might add to my litany:

Good Angel, deliver me - from my original.

Sometimes when my soul is jaunting about, and my heart is wrong end up, I say to myself that nothing matters.

I did not get all that was coming to me, but it is of no account.

Some one says to me, don't be a fool any longer, and you will not feel foolish. When idiotic ideas come into your brain, don't notice them. When you are chump enough to butt into the fire, don't be burned.

This is fine, clear logic, is it not?

The above is sarcasm.

I can be dreadfully sarcastic when I try.

Nothing is nothing.

Anything is nothing.

Everything is nothing.

What has a barrelful of mud in a pig-pen to do with anything.

I am fool's mud.
You probably do not know what fool's mud is. But no matter.

March 18.

Generally speaking, everything depends.
   But, yes, everything matters.
   I must grind and grind away.
   I have no choice.
   In which I resemble a coffee-mill.
   And - I must know that I grind.
   In which I do not resemble a coffee-mill.
   Wherefore, it is plain that I resemble a coffee-mill, yet I do not.
   I wonder, as I write this Betrayal, if there will be one to read it and see the thing that is mingled with [every] word.
   It is the wonderful, intense personality of me.
   I am most marvelously clever.
   And if I have convinced you of this, I am more clever than I thought.
   My conversation hurls itself at your head. When I choose, it makes people turn around in their chairs and stare, giving me all their attention.
   Which may be said of anyone who is noticeably profane.
   Their admiration of me is mixed, decidedly, with other feelings.
   Which is not surprising.
   It is the season of watermelons.
   Therefore, I do not care a damn!

March 19.

On a day when the sky is like lead, and the dreariness of the ash-heap is added to the dreary clouds, there is a deeper gloom about the personality of me.
   The iron enters my soul, and is rusted by the tide of tears within.
   And I feel that I should like to be very naughty. Oh, much more naughty than the naughtiest of the naughty.
   And there comes to me the sweet scent of chrysanthemums. For to the genius the scent of chrysanthemums is sweet, even as the scent of Limburger.
   The racked nerves of my nothingness cry out for a neurotic.
   The vivid phenomena of badness might act as such.
   I would like to live about seven years of judicious badness.
   Oh, divinely beautiful Wickedness!

March 23.

My philosophy, I find after my little analysis, approaches dangerously near to senility.

It is, indeed, strange how one's character can so closely resemble an octagon.

Turn to any side of my character you choose, and you will find it perfectly flat - always flat

Mostly one's acquaintances are fools.

Or, perhaps, I am the fool.

Do you hear?

Perhaps I am the fool.

Genius of my kind must be bad.

That is why my book is so bad.

Which is fortunate.

I get all my little nerves and line them up. They sit up like so many little dogs, begging for food.

So I feed them poison in a spoon.

O, spoon!

I should like to be a real Devil.

A damnably devilish Devil.

If I could be truly wicked, I would jerk myself out of this nothingness by the roots. It is dull, dull, dull! I am unhappy. I feel rotten.

I am alone, and a paralytic philosopher. It is I and the ash-heap. I am odd.

But if the public is as easy for me as it was for my original, I shall soon play even.

*

MISC. JESTS

Mr. Mulcahey And Mrs. Murphy
They Discuss the Life and Works of the Erratic Genius,
Miss Mary MacLane - by Harry J. Lawrence

"Good mornin', Mr. Mulcahey!"

"Good mornin', Mrs. Murphy!"

"'Tis a fine mornin' this mornin', Mr. Mulcahey."

"It is then so, Mrs. Murphy."

"Ye are workin', ye are?"

"No, Mrs. Murphy, not at prisint. Ye see it wor like this. I was swamp-ing on a hay wagon, an' yesterday mornin' we were unloadin' some baled refreshments at a rayspictable institution for transient cayuses, whin the walkin' delegate came along."

"'Hello up there,' sez he."

"'Hello yerself,' sez I."

"'Quit work up there,' sez he."

"'Why so?' sez I."

"'None av yer dom'd business,' sez he. So I quit an' came home."

"Well, I'm sorry I am for ye, Mr. Mulcahey. Faith, th' town seems to be goin' to th' devil."

"It is thin - just - Mrs. Mulcahey; but, speakin' av th' devil, hav' ye read th' Miner lately?"

"I hav' not thin. Ye see th' folks who lived next dure hav' moved, an' I don't know av' any one else in th' neighborhood that would lind me th' loan av' it so. Be afther tellin' me about it, Mr. Mulcahey. Av' course, av' ye hav' th' time."

"Very well so, Mrs. Murphy. Ye see it wor this way. A young lady in th' community writes a ponderous but rather disconnected romance known as 'The' Life av' Mary MacLane,' or 'Save Me a Splinter from Me Sweetheart's Wooden Leg.' After writin' this hair-splittin' epistle Mary discovers she is an ingenuity, and sends her book to th' publisher."

"Excuse me interruptions, Mr. Mulcahey, but what do ingenuity mane?"

"I think it do, Mrs. Murphy, but when th' news become prevalent that Mary made a hit everybody begins to do some stunts in whisperin'. Some say that she is a genius an' others say that she is a fit candidate for th' Acad-emy av' Science.'

"Whin Mary was a little gur-rul she attended school, an' instill av' studyin' her A, B Cs, electricity an' cookery, she smiled a smile to herself an' thin she spoke out: 'Ha, villain! Back to th' woods! Back, back to th' mines. At last I have reached the highest pea knuckle av' fame. Why should I waste me time on such easy dope as a primer. Let me study such men as Marie Back-skirts-off, Virgil, Napoleon, Nick Carter, Bob Ingersoll an' the Divil. Thin observe me smoke as it rises an' disapates in the dreamy, smoky atmosphere.

"'Oh, domn! domn! down! Domn every livin' thing, th' world - th' universe be dom'd!'"

"I beg yer pardon, Mr. Mulcahey, but phwy ar' ye usin' sich profane profanity?"

"That is what Mary sez, Mrs. Murphy."

"Well, excuse me non compus mentus, Mr. Mulcahey, as I wasn't thinkin'. Phwat else?"

"Well, sez she, 'I wants happiness an' hell. I hav' a fine feminine shape.' Talk av' Anna Held - well, Anna never held anything like Mary. Th' rest of th' chapter reads like a testimonial to a pill factory.

"Now, ye ar' no doubt aware av' th' fact, Mrs. Murphy, that we hav' a foine lot av' speciments av' young min in th' community, but Mary sez 'Not if I know it.'

"'T'ell wid em,' sez Mary; 'I will donate thim th' banjo eye an' luv' th' devil. He is so fascinating, so strong - so strong - exactly th' man me wooden heart awaits!'"

"It would that - just - Mr. Mulcahey."

"'I would like to throw mesilf at his head; I would make him a dear little wife. He would luv' me - he would luv'. I'd be in raptures. An' I would luv' him, oh, madly, madly.'

"'Phwat would ye hav' me do, little MacLane?' the devil would say.

"'I would hav' ye lasso me, kangaroo me, maul th' life out av' me, kick in me slats, an' luv' me. Say to me, 'I ye might do a verse or two av' 'Be-ye might do a verve or two av' Because I Luv' ye.'

"'Hurt me; burn me; consume me wid hot luv'; shake me violently, embrace me hard - hard in yer strong, steel lunch-hooks. Let our osculatory exercise be th' limit, wid no bets taken after post time. Giv' me a run for me money, an' thin let me die. Aha! Let me - let me - die - kind devil, let me see me finish.'

"Wouldn't that Gaston an' Alphonse ye, Mr. Mulcahey? Sure, th' gur-rul must be silver tongued."

"I don't know about that, Mrs. Murphy, but I am strongly under the impression that av' she keeps on she will be Silver Bowed."

"'Many times,' sez she, 'I intended to croak mesilf in Silver Bow creek, but changed me mind.'"

"Phwy did she change her mind, Mr. Mulcahey?"

"I don't know, Mrs. Murphy, but I presume she is loike a whole lot av' the miners in Butte."

"In phwat way, Mr. Mulcahey?"

"Well, she don't like to work in the copper water, Mrs. Murphy."

- *Butte Miner* [Montana], 4 May 1902, p 8

Mr. Mulcahey Reviews The Book
He Explains Some of Mary's Monologues to His
Friend Mrs. Murphy - by Harry J. Lawrence

"Good mornin', Mr. Mulcahey!"

"Good mornin', Mrs. Murphy!"

"Is there an-nythng new wid ye, there is?"

"There is, just, Mrs. Murphy, an' be th' powers ye'll be thunder-struck when I'll be afther tellin' ye that they hav' diskivered the' notorious an' obstreperous creatur' that terrorized th' natives av Centerville, Corktown an' Dublin gulch, an' wuz known be th' high-soundin' title av 'Th' Woman in Black,' alias 'Th' Centerville Ghost.'"

"Who wuz th' high an' mighty thafe, Mr. Mulcahey?"

"Well, thot I don't know, Mrs. Murphy, but I have read an' account in wan av th' papers and it lays th' whole thing at th' dure av Mary MacLane."

"Is thot so, Mr. Mulcahey?"

"It is thin, just, Mrs. Murphy. Ye remember I wuz tellin' ye a thing or two about her book last week?"

"Av course, Mr. Mulcahey. Be the way, hov' ye read an-ny more since, ye hov'?"

"I hov', thin, so, and I hov' also a copy av the book."

"Do be afther explainin' a few silictions av th' voluminous undertakin' for me ispicial benefit, Mr. Mulcahey."

"Very well so, Mrs. Murphy. Ye no doubt are undher th' impression thot as long as ye can remember ye hov' bin rayspictable, an' ye wouldn't care to be thrown together, an' shaken up, an' mixed well (as Mary sez) wid a lot av beer jerkers, biscuit shooters an' greasy dagos. Now, wud yez?"

"Not so as ye could notice it, Mr. Mulcahey."

"Well, as I wuz sayin', Mrs. Murphy, Mary didn't do a thing to Butte an' th' people in general. At some Fourth av July she sez, or on a Miners' Union day, 'I agitate me Cinderellas down town an' butt in wid th' common herd. Th' Irish and Cornish predominate,' she says. 'but the Kelleys, Caseys, Calahans, starved-lookin' Chinasers, Finns, Swedes, flea-haunted Indians, an' cigarette min just out av th' bathtub make up th' rest. Av course there are a few from Dogtown (or poetically speakin'), Canineville. Thin there are a few from Busterville, Butchertown an' Chicken flat, otherwise known as Poultry plateau. The rest are seldom seen.'"

"But phwat hav thot to do wid th' ghost, Mr. Mulcahey?"

"Taper off for a phwile, Mrs. Murpry. I'll be comin' to thot prisintly. In regard to her internal economy an' gastronomic machinery, she sez, 'I hov a sound, sinsitiv' liver an' a calm, beautiful stomach, which will digest annything from a spike to a gum boot. Me hear beats like a ragtime melody on a jewsharp. Me lungs are saturated wid the smoky atmosphere until I feel loike a dago pulp roaster. Me insoide workin's don't need an-ny fixin', an' as I sit be th' window of me domestic domicile wid me understandin's shootin' up on th' bureau undher th'e enchantin' spell av a day in October I miditate. Thin it's up to me to percolate th' pike an' wise mesilf phwat th' sulpher smoke has not yit penetrated. I am intensely thankful to the devil for me two good 'trilbys' she says, 'an' I hope he will accept me sincerest gratitude. I lie on th' ground for some minutes an' think. Thin afther aphwile I hov another think comin'. A mon may lie down, but it's a six-to-one-shot he would fall asleep like a dog or a pig an' snore. They're off in Oakland,' she sez, 'so I will chase mesilf back to th' ranch an' put me feet on the bureau. I always,' she sez, 'sit wid me two feet on th' bureau.'"

"Phwat do she put her two feet on th' bureau for, Mr. Mulcahey?"

"Well, Mrs. Murphy, it may be because she hov no footstool, but I suppose av she had four or five pair of feet she would find suitable apartment for all av' thim on th' chaufer."

"On th' - well, th---phwy, on th' bureau, Mrs. Murphy."

"Do she still be stuck on th' devil she do, Mr. Mulcahey?"

"'Tis th' way she is, Mrs. Murphy. His Satanic majesty seems to be a picture card wid th' gur-rul, an' I'm afther presumin' thot it would be no hard job for an-ny wan to win th' divil's home away from him. Think af me,' she sez, 'livin' wid th' devil. Me grandest possibility will be realized. An' in th' soft, black night I will lie be th' side av th' man-divil, an' me head will rist in th' hollow av his shouldher an' me lunch-hook will be clasped in his lunch-hook, an' me feet will be up on th' bureau. Always on th' bureau. 'Be happy now, me weary little wife,' the devil will say. 'Well, I should smoke a rope,' I shall reply. 'Phwat can I accommodate ye wid,' he will ask. An' thin I will say, 'Oh, devil, devil, devil! Oh, misery, misery of nothingness! Give, oh, pass me out some happiness. Phwy don't ye come, kind devil, an' stay wid me always?' 'Look me in the face,' I will say, 'an' blat into me listening ear that I'm a Marie Backskirtsoff - a Napoleon. Say to me thot although me moustache has disappeared, th' eyebrows still remains. Tell me that ye luv me devil. Say to me those words, oh, devil, devil, devil, devil, devil.'"

"Th' devil, domn th' devil, Mr. Mulcahey. Is it goin' bughouse ye ar're?"

"No, it is hardy thot bad, Mrs. Murphy; only I wor' just throwin' wan av Mary's favorite monologues out av me for yer sensitive nerves."

"Well, Mr. Mulcahey, I av th' opinion thot me sound, sinsitve nerves ar-re not quite equal to th' occasion. But, not goin' aside from th' subject, tho', wouldn't that book 'Mike the Milkman Ye?'

"It's the way it wud, Mrs. Murphy. It wud almost jar yer mother's preserves. Ye kin hov' th' lind av it whin I get it back from the Caseys, Kellys an' Callahans."

"Well, do ye still think Mary is full av prunes, Mr. Mulcahey?"

"No, Mrs. Murphy; only full av th' devil."

- *Butte Miner* [Montana], 12 May 1902, p unknown

The Old-Timer's Opinion
A Few Remarks on Mary MacLane by an Old-time Cowboy
"Mary MacLane," said the old-time stockman, after reading a few choice extracts from her latest production, "is a likely filly and owns a vocabulary that out-paces Hurricane Bill and puts Calamity Jane in the same bunch with the ice wagon. Looks ter me as if she needs halter breaking or a long spell on a matrimonial picket rope so as to kinder get her used to the ways of civilization nowadays.

"For a nineteen-year-old, it seems ter me as if she's grazed over a heap of range and maybe run up against a corral somewhere that makes her show the white of her eyes every time anyone tries to head her off. The way she damns everything in general puts me in mind of the time when I was driving a bunch of dogies on the Upper Judith and met old Dud Rickard where he was stuck in the mud on Skull creek with ten and three wagons loaded with wool and it was rainin' like H - a-beatin' tanbark. He cussed the world by sections and called on the old boy with the split hoofs to come up and stick his pitchfork into the off wheeler and make him get inter the collar. He wouldn't show up, however, and Dud tried the next best thing - the black-snake. That's the way it will be with Mary; when she finds she can't raise the devil she'll take the next best thing, and I'm a-thinkin' that will have to be a good imitation of the real article. By the gee whiz! the gals nowadays are getting altogether too rollicky, anyway," said the old stockman as he puffed meditatively at his cigar.

- *Fergus County Argus* [Lewistown, Montana], 7 May 1902, p 6

A la Mary MacLane
"O, blankety blank!" exclaimed the soubrette, clasping her hands. "Blank it! Blank everybody. Blank everything! Blank! Blank! Blank! Blank!"

"What's the matter with you?" asked the heavy villain, in astonishment.

"I'm trying to be happy!" signed the soubrette.
- *Harford Courant* [Connecticut], 19 May 1902, p 15

Mary MacLane Again

Editor Buffalo Express: - Since seeing John Smith's verse two week so ago "Mary wrote a little book," etc. , I have perused The Story of Mary MacLane and I was thereby moved to express my feelings in enclosed verse which you may print if you care to. - M.S.P. Buffalo, June 8th.

*

O Mary MacLane, / You give me a pain, / With your longings and burnings and such; / You ask a great deal. / But I tremblingly feel / That the devil may send you o'ermuch.
- *Buffalo Express* [New York], 14 Jun 1902, p 7

From a Forthcoming Book Entitled Betrayal of John Smith O'Lyin

I do not begin this volume by printing a picture of myself as a frontispiece.

The whole book is to be a picture of myself. If any one who reads this book cannot tell exactly how I look, he will be lacking in soulful penetration. It is a bad thing to lack soulful penetration. One never can become a successful bill collector without it.

Besides, I don't see how anybody can be interested in knowing how I look except people whom I owe. And the sooner they forget me, the better.

Moreover, I have no picture of myself. And it costs money to get a picture taken. And I have no money. There's the plain truth about the absence of a picture at last.

I do not call this book a Portrayal, or a Portraiture, or a Confession, or a Recollection, or a Memoir (please don't pronounce it Meam-war). I've been scooped on all those titles. Besides, that would sound too much as if I were imitating the joyous Mary MacLane of Butte, aha! (How would that do for the first line of a topical song?) And, of course, anybody can see that I have not taken the slightest hint of a suggestion from the Montana Sweet Marie, who spells her Genius with a big, big G, and curses the world with a big, big D. O, dear, no! No more than she did from Marie Bashkirtseff. (Anybody who had to spell such a name as that every time she wrote a check was excusable for being sour on civilization.)

No; I call this my Betrayal. I am going to betray myself, to give myself away, to tell all the things about myself that I don't want anybody to know, or at least everything that I ought not to want anybody to know. I purpose to lay bare all the hidden recesses of my tumultuous soul. I once saw a professor of anatomy hold up a human head before his class with his two hands and, after the youthful searchers for knowledge had been properly thrilled, pull it apart into halves - it had previously been split - and turn the halves around to show the inside of the head. That is what I am going to do with my head in a figurative sense.

And why do I write this Betrayal? For Fame? Not much: I've been a reporter. I've seen Fame from behind its coattails. I've been inside the factory where Fame turns out its rush orders. In emergencies I've helped stuff the excelsior in some of the Fame factory's choicest products. I have helped to stamp the trademark on it and pack it up in burlaps and ship it to its destination.

But perhaps, then, you may think I feel myself inspired with burning thoughts that must find outlet; that I write because some unseen, irresistible force tells me I must.

Guess again.

I've heard of people who claimed to feel that way. But the only chance they have to get into the newspapers is through the Vox Populi column. My advice to anybody who has got the soul-longing literary disease is to learn to write ads. There's no better way for a soul-longing, literary mind to let itself out than by extolling the merits of Scrubeen's soap and Curem's pills.

I am not a peripatetic philosopher. If I do any peripateting, it's not for the philosophy of it, but because I haven't carfare.

I am an aerostatic philosopher. You may decide for yourselves what that is. I don't know.

This world is a hollow sphere with the hollowness on the outside.

I don't like fresh young onions from California. I prefer they should come from Hamburg, if at all.

I don't worship the Devil. If the Devil is a refined, accomplished man, as Heins affirmed and Mary MacLane supposes, he is probably a cad. Most refined, accomplished men who try to be devilish are. If he has a cloven hoof and a forked tail, he must be a beast, somewhat resembling an ox. If I had such a Devil, I'd send him to an abattoir and make porterhouse steaks of him.

Being a man, I suppose I ought to conceive the Devil as something feminine. I might get up a very good female devil out of novels I have read, but personally I never saw a female try to assume a Satanic role that she did not burlesque it.

I have begun to doubt if there is any Devil for men. All the literary people who claim to have known him have described a Devil for women, especially for silly young girls of nineteen.

Here is the aerostatic philosopher's explanation of volcanic eruptions and earthquakes: The world being hollow on the outside, Nature must constantly strive to fill up its hollowness. When Nature gets the outside of the world filled up and the inside properly hollowed out, perhaps we shall all like it better.

This being the last chapter, I think I ought to answer the puzzle given somewhere toward the front of the book as to why I have written this Betrayal.

It's because I want money.

I want money so I can have a dining room big enough to play ping-pong in.

I want money enough so I won't have to wear a laundered shirt two days in succession.

I want money enough so I can own an automobile.

I want money enough so I can afford to buy a book when I wish to read one.

I want money enough so I can have my shoes polished by a dirty-faced Italian boy every day.

I want money enough so I can become a Prominent Citizen and always look solemn and serious.

If enough idiots will buy this book so I can get $5,000 from the sale of it, it will have achieved its purpose.

- John Smith

- *Buffalo Express* [New York], 26 May 1902, p 6

Note And Comment - By Frank Putnam
Poor Little Mary MacLane

From Butte, which is commonly mute, / Comes a cry of ecstatical pain; / From Butte - God preserve us! - from Butte, / Given over to guzzling and gain. / Like the sobbing night winds that dispute / In a minor that saddens the rain; - / Like a heart-break blown into a flute, / Is the story of Mary MacLane.

Mary, Mary, quite contrary, / Born to be loved and slain; -
Poor little Mary, - out of the dark. / And into the dark again.

She loves and repels - tis' her sex; / She desires, and fears her desire; / Like a nymph she coquettishly flecks / Her eyeballs with amorous fire; / She calls on the Devil to fly / To her succor, but calls him in vain : - / He is busy with those who defy / *His* wishes. - *Poor* Mary MacLane!

Mary, Mary, quite contrary, / (Give her your love, not blame)
Poor little Mary, pawn of the Fates / In a truly mysterious game.

From Boston, the prude by the sea, / To Butte, is a million of miles, / In the matter of rye vs. tea / And the standards of ethical styles; / But the prude by the Puritan sea, / In spite of her centuried skein, / Has woven no music for me / Like the sorrow of Mary MacLane

Mary, Mary, quite contrary, / Beating against your bars, -
You should have been born in the earth's grey morn, / When Venus
was conquering Mars.

But now, O ye Gods! and in Butte! / Was ever such vile trick played / On a spirit lit with a Sapphic fire / And housed in a winsome maid? / 'Tis a tale for the after years, / To be read with a tender sigh / By maids who scan through a mist of tears / The same old baffling sky.

Mary, Mary, quite contrary, / Born to be loved and slain; -
Poor little Mary, - out of the dark, / And into the dark again.

- *National Magazine,* Jul 1902, p 441

Another Genius

"You say your daughter goes around telling the neighbors that you are no good?"

"Yes," answered the young woman's father.

"And she turns up her nose at work of any kind?"

"She'd have a fit if anybody asked her to help wash dishes."

"And are the reports true that she says things which shock the minister when he comes to call?"

"I'm afraid they are."

"Aren't you going to do something about it?"

"I don't know what to do. I don't know whether to get angry or to try to feel proud because we have a Mary MacLane in the family."

- *Evening Star* [Washington, D.C.], 17 Jul 1902, p 4

Have You Heard About Mary MacLane?

Being a merry catch after the fashion of "The Widow Malone."

Have you heard about Mary MacLane? / So vain! / Who comes from Montana's dry plain; / No rain! / She has written a book, / Which the same it has "took," / She has, this same Mary MacLane / So vain! // 'Twill give you, this book of MacLane, / A pain! / If you read it you'll nigh go insane / Murrain! / For Whitman's not in it / No, not for a minute / With the toughness of Mary MacLane / Unclane! / With the toughness of Mary MacLane. // She's not modest is Mary MacLane / So vain! / She hopes to win laurels like Crane, / Or Taine! / "It's a janious I am, / An' I don't give a damn, / So the critics an' all may complain / In vain! / So the critics an' all may complain." // She's one wish, has this Mary MacLane, / So vain! / To be wed with the divil, she'd fain, Insane! / "No, not on your life, / Will I have you for wife!" / Said the divil to Mary MacLane, / So vain! / Said the divil to Mary MacLane. // After radin' this book of MacLane, / So vain! / You rip it an' tear it amain / In twain! / If

this sort of thing wins / Praise bol she's not twins! / There's only one Mary MacLane, / So vain! There's only one Mary MacLane.
- *Chicago Daily Tribune*, 26 Jul 1902, p B17

"Mary McLane has been in town. I didn't see her, me place not bein' a raysort f'r th' young an' yearnin', an' especially me duckin' all lithry ladies iv whativer sex. Mary McLane is th' author iv a book called: 'Whin I am older I'll know betther.' Ye ought to read it, Hinnissey.'"
- *Boston Daily Globe*, 27 Jul 1902, p 41; reprinted in Anon. [Dunne, Finley Peter]: *Observations by Mr. Dooley*, Harper & Brothers, New York, 1902, p 185

The West is very much excited over the eastern triumphal progression of Miss Mary MacLane. Hence, the "Limerick:"
There was a young woman of Butte, / A wild, wooly western galoot / She said, "Damn! Damn! Damn! / I'm a genius, I am!" / And Chicago said, "Isn't she cute?" - New York Sun
- *Los Angeles Times*, 27 Jul 1902, p B1

From Mary MacLane - Via Baltimore

Boston, July 23 - I look out of my window, and what do I see?
Beans.
I look in the papers, and what do I see?
Beans.
I go through the house, and what do I see?
Beans.
I go to the theatre, and what do I hear?
Beans.
I move in society, and what do I hear?
Beans.
Butte has her sand and her dank, dreary hills, but she is free from beans. She may be short on culture, but she is short of beans.
What is an education, if it must be coated with beans?
I have not found my dear devil yet, but I have found beans, and that is near enough. - Baltimore American.
- *Boston Daily Globe*, 28 Jul 1902, p 6

Mary MacLane's Mother

My maw, she keeps a-hustlin' f'm mornin' till th' night, / Cleanin' up an' gittin' order where th' things is jest a sight. / Chuckin' cobwebs f'm the ceilin', throwing carpets out th' door. / There's dad's collar t' be bunted, Charlie's

buttons t' sew on. / An' her work keeps on a-growin' till she never gits it done; / An' on the' sofa, loafin', is my great big sister Mary, / Who ain't performed a stroke o' work since she turned literary! / My maw's the hardest worker that th' town has ever seen - / She works all day an' works all night an' hustles all between; / Th' way she keeps a-goin' is a mystery t' me / But she does, an jest as cheerful as a mother ought t' be. / Why, we never heard a cross word, even when she's nearly dead. / An' she sorter smiles when told that Mary's loafin' up in bed! / My maw's an awful hustler, but that lazy, loafin' Mary / Ain't got a live bone in her since she's turned out literary! / It seems t' me things ain't divided right w'en maw must work / An' Mary lay a-snoozin' like a great big loafin' Turk - / It seems t' me that Mary ought t' tumble out o' bed / An' git dish-washin' notions in her literary head! / But maw says it's all right, becuz w'n folks git struck that way / They don't seem fit f'r nothin' but t' loaf an' dream all day! / Yet I can't help a thinkin' that th' world has got contrary. / An' Mary ought t' hustle an' let maw get literary! - Baltimore News
  - *Malone Farmer* [New York], *c.* Jul 1902, p unknown

Soul Versus Stomach
Correspondence between Mary MacLane and
Richard Le Gallienne - by W.J.W.
The News Letter has, without the least bit of trouble or expense, secured a number of letters that might have passed between Mary MacLane and Mr. Richard Le Gallienne - Mary, the apostle of gourmandism, who likes her meat raw and dripping, and Richard, to whom wine and great grapes, with candied violet petals for dessert, make a satisfying and exalting meal. If you wish to know whether or not these are genuine letters, write to either Richard or Mary, giving your full name and address and enclose stamps.

*

My Dear Richard:
  Joy is in me. The devil, for whom I have longed, is raging my soul, trampling with his cloven hoofs over my red heart, jabbing his pointed tail into my eyes and blinding me to everything but his supreme beauty. Oh, Richard, I have just eaten - just eaten, Richard, than which nothing could be more divine. I had mush - thick mush with plenty of sugar and great gobs of coagulated cream. And I had a quart of olives, each one of which, as it went its salty way down my superbly beautiful throat, gave me sensations enough for pages of copy. I had beer and garlic, too, and now I am smoking a cigarette. Do you think any of my family, whom I hate, would come around me now?
  Richard, if you could only see me, to know for sure how beautiful I am!

The sun never shone upon anything so divine, so queenly - and my brilliant mind is the only thing that matches my form and face. Ain't I got a nerve?

O, how I despise my family. The whole damned layout of them use tooth brushes.

Feverishly, hungrily,
Mary

Dear Mary:

Why do you reveal the hairy side of your soul to me? I always want to think of you as living on hot Montana air, and here you are spending your royalties on mush and cigarettes - men's cigarettes, too, no doubt. Was it oatmeal mush, dearest? O, don't say it was! Tell me, rather, that you wrote figuratively when you told me of your mush, or at least, that it was made of rose leaves boiled in dew. Do!

I dreamed of you last night, dearest one. I dreamed that you were a Golden Girl - is it gold or silver they raise in Montana? - and that you were sitting on a cloudlet, and I beside you. We were figuring royalties and planning a lecture tour, except when people went by; then we would hold hands and look yearningly into each other's eyes.

I have just finished combing my hair, love, and I am going out into the garden to hear the birdies sing. I think I can get dope for about a column.

Farewell, beloved. My soul is your soul, and your soul is my soul, and - there, darn it, I'm all tangled up. If there was cash in sight I might finish it. As it is, you can find plenty of things near enough like it in any of my books. Boost me whenever you get a chance; tell people how deuced eccentric I am.

Fakily,
Richard

Dear Richard:

There's the devil to pay. My hated mother and I had a dispute as to whether we would have corned beef or kidney stew for dinner, and to subdue the wild storm that is raging within my tempestuous soul, I have been sticking pins through my little brother's ears.

I could eat a whale fried in its own blubber, Richard, with stewed seaweed on the side. O, how hungry I am - how I yearn and yearn and yearn for a French dinner. You know the French dinners are rotten here. I am going to get out of this rank hole, where nobody appreciates me - out into the wide world, where there is an opportunity for such a genius as I am. I have always wanted to eat a nigger. Let us go to the South Seas, Richard. You milk the cocoanuts and I'll kill niggers, and life will be a grand and gory barbecue.

You've no idea what a wonder I am. Honest, I'm a peach - but not a fuzzy peach. Everybody rubbers at me when I walk along the streets, I am so beautiful.

How I long to be wicked - to just make things sizz. And how I hate my family - my despised father and mother and brothers and sisters, who insist on cooking their meat, and do not want me to smoke black cigars. I'm a glutton for excitement, Richard, I'm going to put on a pair of spurs and go out and ride a steer. I - I - I - I - this letter is all I, and I am the greatest thing that ever warmed the whole atmosphere with my presence. For I am Mary MacLane, the great Montana meat-eater, whose stomach always yearns.

Isn't my book a daisy? If the vulgar public only recognized my genius as I do I would make enough off of it to corner the grub market of the world.

Strenuously, passionately yours,
Mary

- San Francisco News Letter, 2 Aug 1902, p 17

Murmurings of Mary MacLane

I saw the New York base ball team play the Chicago's [*sic.*] today. The New York team is a scrub one. I love to scrub. I shall go [*sic.*] in New York.

I met an Italian just from Italy yesterday. I spoke to him but he could not understand me. Nobody understands me.

I looked at my toothbrush this morning. I examined the bristles carefully. Then I burst into tears. I did not know why I wept because the bristles were once on the hog. They are that way now.

I have been going to a printing office for some time past. Do you want to know why? Because I love the devil.

I always thought I was the most beautiful girl in the world until I saw a half tone picture of myself. How can I now consider myself a beaut from Butte? I always wanted to be pretty as a picture too.

I cried again today. I had thought of the most beautifully insulting thing to say to my father - and I forgot it. - New York Sun

- Cedar Rapids Republican, 9 Sep 1902, p 4

The Mary MacLane Spirit

We can, perhaps, best illustrate the Mary MacLane spirit by reproducing the following sketch of Mary McJane, servant girl, from The New York Evening Sun, which shows precisely what the literary Mary would have felt and done had fate made her only an autocrat of the dishrag instead of the pen:

"I am a hard proposition!

"They don't know me in this flat!

"Third place in a week, and today I've broken only one cut-glass sugar bowl and two china cups!

"Bah! My hands are getting too steady!

"The woman said she expected me to work! Me! And my wages only $32 a month!

"I'll go in the parlor and kick her dog!

"I love to hurt dogs! I suppose that is the devil in my nature - or the beer!

"I wonder where they keep the wine!

"There! I have dropped the meat dish! I'll tell the mistress. Perhaps she will want to save the pieces! The crash of breaking china is music to my ears!

"I wonder why she loves her husband! He has made goo-goo eyes at me only once! Think I'll look for another place! No, not today! The parlor curtains are real lace; I'll tear them before I go.

"Wish the mistress would leave her writing desk open. Then I could spill the ink on the piano keys.

"Plush-covered furniture in a Harlem flat! Bah! I'll give them notice to change it!

"I was not born for joy! I could not smile when they choked on the coffee. I had put red pepper in it. Tomorrow I'll put soap in the waffles.

"Tonight I shall walk under the stars. I may meet a policeman by the door of the family entrance to Casey's.

"I wonder why some girls stay a week in one place! How monotony must grind into their lives. But I suppose they cannot all be Mary McJanes.

"I grow weary trying to be good. I must break a dinner plate and spoil the set!

"In my next place I shall take the mornings out as well as the afternoons.

"There is a feeling of heaviness inside me. The cooking of this mistress does not agree with me, and it brings on the wicket feeling.

"I feel that I am not long for this place!

"I cannot trust myself to write any more!"
- *Atlanta Constitution*, 21 Sep 1902, p D8

A Letter From the Interior
by An Outsider

An' I jes' want ter tell you, too, thet thair haint a feller ever so low down, I don't care hoo he is, but thet their feller wants to git up in the worl' and be suthin'- or to'ther. It's jest born in 'em. I knowed that long ago from my own ixperience, and I seen it in print sinct. Some gurl out west, name o' Mary Mac Lane, has writ all about ut in a book, &'wot is in print is so. Don't know when i have looked in a boock thet kindo' said just what I'd 'a' said my own self if th' Almighty'd 'a' gave me the gift o' penwork.

Ja know? When I was 19 I was jist thet way myself - like this here Mary says she is now - i thot I was jist ekil to anythink thet would turn up. And Lord how I did ache fer suthin' tu turn up! Me and Bill Peters used ter talk ut all over how we wuz goin' to be these here millionairs that ye read so much about. Bill thot he was a heap smarter nor I wuz - an' Lord, I never said nothin' but ut made me snicker up my' sleeve to hear thet feller talk knowin' how easy I was gonto walk right on ahead of him and one day take him ridin' on my steam yawt. That was 20 year back. Bill's tendin' store now fer Mosie Patterson over tu Buckville, an' i have my' 20 akers. But say, that there Mary McLane has spoke out jist what a man feels while he's jist naturally waitin' 20 year fer suthin' to turn up. We all feels thet way', I reckon. It's all powerful true, whut Mary says. An' I bet you Mary thinks all the while how smart she is coz she's writ that boock - when tain't nothin' but jist wot everybody that's pushed down in this cruel worl' could rite if they' only knowed how tu spell.

Mary, she rites elegant like and sad, - "Never does the pitiable barren emptiness of my life come upon me with so intense a force as when my eyes light up at the site of them six tooth brushes in the bathroom. Every Friday an' every Friday to see nawthink but them there six pesky' tooth brushes - why its sutthin offle!" That's jist it. Ja know? I started out same as that Mary', a thinkin' 'at i wuz suthin' worth while, 't i was "it," an' ace high, an' all thet. And now i go out over mi 20 akers and look at them weeds, or the weat is down mebby, - knocked down by' a storm, er else the dry weather is puckerin' ut all up - jist them 'ere 20 akers an' no more. An' then i look down at mi torn breeches!...

But this here Mary MacLane's gave me an idear. If she can raise a row about it, wy i can tew, by golly. And so, I thot'i'd rite tew you and ast you ef you new wear I could find a feller to print a little suthin'an' how mutch I'd likely git out of ut. Coz I haint agointo take no trouble fer nawthink. But ef there's any chanct o' gettin' anythink printed, an' any chanct o' makin' suthin' out of ut, wy i'm there every time, you bet. Wouln't ut be a joke ef one o' these days I'd be ridin' Bill Peters around in my yawt yet, made my fortion outa ritin' wot a cruil and barren & offle place this yere worl's grown to be? Eh, Bill?

- *Young Men's Home Journal*, Sep 1902, pp 27-29

As It Might Have Been
From the New York Herald of December 26, 1902:

... Ye editor was made happy yesterday by receiving a lump of coal weighing ten pounds. It was the handsomest Christmas gift he received.... The literary editor begs leave to announce the receipt of a new edition of Mary

MacLane from the thoughtful publisher. - Memphis Commercial Appeal
- *Houston Daily Post*, 21 Oct 1902, p 6

When she led him around to the Subject of the late Novels he got all balled up, for he thought that Gertrude Atherton wrote "Mary MacLane."
- Ade, George: *The Girl Proposition: A Bunch of He and She Fables*, R.H. Russell, New York, [*c*. Nov.] 1902, p 75

Miscellany
Misunderstood
If no one understands you, and you are soulful and bilious, and hate yourself and despise the world, and want to screech and be sentimental and foolish, and so on, don't be a Mary MacLane and write it. Hunt up a condemned man and tell him all about it; but be absolutely certain that he is going to be hung early next morning. - From Puck
- *Western Dental Journal*, Dec 1902, p 565

[Cartoon illus.] - Senator Wm. A. Clark, of Butte, Montana, a town noted chiefly for having produced the greatest genius of the day, Mary MacLane, the author of "I am it."
- Fleming, Thomas: *Around the Capital with Uncle Hank - Recorded Together With Many Pictures*, Nutshell Pub. Co, New York, 1902, p 53

The Story of Nathan L. Todd
January First
I, belonging, I suppose I shall have to admit, to my own race, and eighty-five years old, am going to write myself up, and see if I can't get it printed. And I do not see why I haven't as good a right to do so, as Mary MacLane has her pieces.
January Second
I am a genius, a philosopher of my own school, a versatile duck, and exceedingly, exceedingly singular.

I can't appear to find any one, anywhere or in any sort of shape, that comes anywhere near coming up to me. There are also no persons now living who understand me: and the subject is so vast, that I am not always quite sure whether I understand myself.

January Fifth
There are only two different people in all history that come anywhere near me in ability, and I can discount them and give them a hundred on the string. Shakespeare, I will admit, said several things that I should have said, in rather better form, if I had only had time. The other is John L. Sullivan.

Sullivan has some philosophy - everybody knows that: but I - I - I - I - am wholesale and retail agent for it.

In one thing, however, I resemble several others of my own race, very largely - I steal.

Yes, reader, I steal, and occasionally get caught at it.

February Thirteenth

I care nothing for laws or rules, although I am exceedingly willing to live under their protection. I am a genius, you see.

Yet the world thus far does not seem to have ascertained the fact that I am a genius - although I have frequently given it full information upon the subject. I sometimes wonder, when lying in the rather close quarters which the state allots me, whether the angels do not have regular crying-spells over the fact that it is not generally known that I am a genius - while it is generally known that I am a thief.

Oh, rats, rats, rats, rats, rats, rats!

March Second

I once had a kind and indulgent motherinlaw, and lived several years, in comparative comfort, at her expense. But we fell out at last: for her tooth-brush did not please me. It had a bone handle, while mine was of ivory (one that I had borrowed out of a show-case while the pharmacist was dispensing soda-water at the other counter) and we could not, would not, agree any longer.

My father, mother, sisters, brothers, cousins, aunties, uncles, and in-laws, were all too ordinary for any sort of use: not one of them amounted to a little bit: only I - I - I - was the real thing.

How I do love that pronoun of the first person and singular number! It is the only one worth considering. I generally kiss it and put my forehead on it immediately after writing it.

March Fourth

My ancestors did not amount to anything, either - except as my progenitors. They lived, loved, hated, fought, bled, died, and smashed around the world generally-not on their own account, at any possible date: it was all for Me. They had Me in their minds when they did all these things. The whole shooting-match culminates in Me, you see.

I am an analyzer. I analyze everything. I analyze my friends, and also my foes - none of whom have the least tip as to my own interior convolutions.

I analyze myself. I commenced self-analysis at a very early age. At six months of age, I analyzed certain portions of my cuticle with a butcher knife that had been thoughtfully left within my reach. At the tender age of one year, I analyzed one of my toes with a hammer. I do not confine my analysis to people themselves: but extend the industry to their portemonnaies whenever I get a chance.

By diligent analysis, I have ascertained that I have a heart composed of cord-wood. But the same cannot be asserted of my head - oh no - no - no - no!

It may be of interest to the world, that when I sit down on my humble little cot, to write these pleasant little memoirs, I cross my left leg over my right, and shortly afterwards my right leg over my left, and so on.

I am a genius.

I am most fascinatingly original, and bewitchingly odd. I am also well set up - in business, for a term of years. The world contains not my parallel of latitude, and it is a good thing for the world.

I am a quiet, inoffensive little man, with several plain features; but when I get up upon my hind feet and howl, then please stand from under, and from over, and from all around there!

I have never injured any of my vital or victual organs, and it may be interesting to the public to know how I eat a slice of bacon. It is an art, and the great wide hungry world should know that I - I - have acquired the art of eating bacon.

First, through the generosity of others, I procure the bacon. Then I take a good look at it, to be sure it is there. Then I think for a moment of the beautiful porcine animal from which it came. I think also of the snug sty in which he dwelt.

I then do this bacon the honor of taking a small neat little nip at it. Strange to say, I eat when I am hungry, and am hungry when I eat. I am a genius.

As I do the bacon the honor of biting it, I reflect on what a wicked old fellow the hog probably was, anyhow. My mouth becomes a happy mouth. A change takes place throughout my whole nature - physical, mental, and immoral.

It may be interesting to the public to know that after I have masticated the bacon, it slips down into my stomach. I am a genius.

My stomach immediately bursts forth in beautiful song. I stand upon my head, and wave my feet in the air.

For further details, consult any good physiology. But I have no doubt that the whole world will envy me, when it knows how well I enjoy a slice of bacon.

I have been looking over the life of Jesse James. He was a little like me, but nowhere near equal.

When I die, will anybody weep over me? I do not see how they can help it: but still I feel that I am not more than half understood. My life is filled with self; I am something of a liar; I steal, and am proud of it; I am ever so many things that I don't appear to be; I am yearning to get on intimate terms with his Satanic Majesty; I am a kind of an everlasting upstart of a nuisance generally: and yet - and yet - the world will not admire and adore me! I can't understand it. Why am I not of and in the galloping herd? Because the world does not understand me, and has put me in a stall.

Yet sometimes I think the Morning Glory Gentleman understands me: though I know all the time that he doesn't. He is a sheriff who once, when I was in his care, treated me kindly in order to get along with me. I am extraordinary. I am way ahead of anything that ever existed.

I have 2,156 pictures of Lucrezia Borgia, and love every one of them, although no two are alike. Every one of them, however, is strong.

I have a measly suspicion that when I get a little older, I shall become a very insignificant no-account person: and if this little schoolboy-composition brings me fame, I'm going to make the most of it while I can. Wouldn't you?

- *Nathan L. Todd*

- *Every Where*, month unknown, 1902 [vol 11, no 2], pp 54-55

Albany Day by Day
Plaint For Mary M'lane

Oh, I sit and watch and I sit and wait, / Oh, how long must I wait in vain, / What alls your genius? Why, don't you write? / Speak a little, Mary MacLane. / Have you done it at last? Are you down in the hole? / Do you suffer still with that same strange pain? / Do you still dream dreams on the hills of Butte? / Speak and answer, Mary MacLane. // Is that same lime-barrel in the vacant lot? / Are your cheeks still brown with the sun and rain? / Is your tooth brush still on the bath room shelf? / Are you married yet, Mary MacLane?

- *Abegweit*

- *Albany Evening Journal* [New York], 11 Apr 1903, p 6

The Co-Operative Novel Association
By Carolyn Wells

"Now we must consider style," says the chairman, and first off they all thought he meant fashions, but he didn't; he meant things like grammar and spelling, and yet not exactly those either ... we've got to have somebody later on in the book that'll make things hum. Some one just as great on style, you know, but different."

The others agreed to this, and they picked out Marie Corelli and Mary MacLane, who are considered awfully stylish.

Then for realism in general they took W.D. Howells, but for special realistic occurrences they chose others - like Mary Adams for tears and kisses, and Hall Caine for sad and gloomy bits.

- *Frank Leslie's Popular Monthly*, Apr 1903, p 645

Woman's Column
Neway [sic.] Items to Interest the Fair Sex

Mary McLane is writing a novel on the "Trials and Temptations of a Shop Gurl."

- *Weekly Observer* [Marcellus, New York], mid-1903, p unknown

Albany Day by Day
Happy Again

I have waited long with a heavy heart, / So patient and silent and meek, / With my eyes on the news and my ear to the West, / For Mary Maclane [sic.] to speak. // And now I am happy and full content, / There's nothing the matter with me, / For Mary Maclane [sic.] is going to speak / Of herself and Annabel Lee.

- Abegweit

- *Albany Evening Journal* [New York], 19 Aug 1903, p 6

Albany Day by Day

It breaks my heart to think it. / It is not the proper caper / That Mary McLane should go to work / On a Denver daily paper. // What is the devil thinking of / That he should have her do it? / Or did she take the job so quick / The devil never knew it[?]

- Abegweit

- *Albany Evening Journal* [New York], 12 Oct 1903, p 6

Idle Thoughts of an Idle Fellow

We hasten to extend congratulations to the unselected, but inevitable, husband of Mary MacLane. She will write her opinion of him in a book, instead of orating to him. The man will be envied when the vast army of Henry Penheckers learns that he can stay out until 2 a.m. and hear nothing when he carries his shoes up the stairs except the mad, swift click of Mary's typewriter.

- *Elmira Telegram* [New York], 8 Nov 1903, p unknown

MacGinniss' Imagination

Pause and ponder on the imagination of the Hon. John MacGinniss. 'Tis a fearful and a wonderful thing. The longer it stays away from Butte the greater it grows. Butte is a practical place where poetry and romance and flights of

imagination do not thrive, but when a budding and healthy imagination like that of Mr. MacGinniss is removed to the more congenial atmosphere of Chicago, the modern Athens, it spreads and expands and blossoms forth like a Thanksgiving day chrysanthemum ... Verily, the MacGinniss imagination in the rarified atmosphere of Chicago glows and illuminates like a bunch of arc lights on a dark night. As a producer of romance it has the Mary MacLane imagination driven to the tall timber.
- *Butte Inter Mountain* [Montana], 19 Nov 1903, p 4

Pretty Much Everything
Mary MacLane
Book I., by the Lady from Butte, / Being naughty, some folks thought it cutte. / Book II, being tame. / Didn't sell quite the same - / Though it bettered the lady's reputte. - The Reader
- *Auburn Bulletin* [New York], 3 Dec 1903, p 3.

The Garbage man handed me the following and said he found it in the waste basket of a jolly good fellow. I print it for all its worth and more too.
I've read the sad story of Mary McLane / And (if slang is permitted) it gives me a pain / Sweet Mary, dear Mary, go back to the woods / I don't like to say it but you don't have the goods / You're waiting the coming of the devil you say / I hope he will get you and fly far away.
- *The Ghourki*, [specific date unknown], [vol. 2] 1902-1903, p 449

Devil
[Cartoon illus.] An old rascal mentioned in the Bible, now reported engaged to Mary McLane.
- Wurdz, Gideon [pseud., Charles Wayland Towne]: *The Foolish Dictionary*, John W. Luce & Co., [May] 1904, no pg. numbers but *c.* p 34

My Diary
May 24, 1903
... I am going to give to this book "chips from my mind," as Mary McLane says. Oh, she's a genius. I saw a picture of her once.
Of course, I shall write here only those things which I would not tell to anyone, not even to my closest chum at the Club. Everything will be plain and sincere, worthy of my choice.
Yesterday I went to Temple. A strange rabbi gave the sermon....
August 30, 1904
Farewell, little book! You have served me well. I can give you no more ap-

propriate ending than to say you will truly be of service to the world, if you honestly portray the feelings of one whom Professor Dummeszeugsprecher was proud to call his friend! -

- *Eupheonisbia Buenette Le Vay - at the Villa D'Argent - (A.L.S.)*
- *Hebrew Union College Annual,* Jul 1904, p 247

Where ignorance is Bliss Carman, 'tis folly to be wise.
One touch of Kipling makes the whole world Kim.
One must have a long spoon to eat with Mary MacLane.
- Wells, Carolyn: *Folly for the Wise,* Bobbs-Merrill Co., Indianapolis, [Oct.] 1904, p 98

And those who made a Mint off Miss MacLane, / And those who shuddered at her Jests profane, / Alike consigned her to Oblivion, / And buried once, would not dig up again.
- Burgess, Gelett: *The Rubaiyat Of Omar Cayenne,* Frederick A. Stokes Co., New York, [Dec.] 1904, p 9

Butte, Montana
by Robert J. Shores

[Illus. cartoon] There are many persons rated queer, / Have come from Butte - Montana, / It's [*sic*] fame has spread both far and near, / The fame of Butte - Montana; / There's Mary MacLane and Jack Munroe / And Senator Clark and well, you know / They even claimed Jean Jack Rosseau [*sic*] / Out there in Butte - Montana. // The Dealer is ready to take a drink, / Out there in Butte - Montana, You seldom get the rinkey-dink, / 'Way out in Butte - Montana; / The cub reporter gets twenty per / To call him "spendthrift" is no slur. / The city ed don't give you - er - / Well, hell, in Butte - Montana. // They haven't a tree or a real live flower, / Out there in Butte - Montana, / But toadies blossom every hour - / 'Way out in Butte - Montana; / There's hardly a cherry nor olive grows / Excepting the kind that paints your nose - / But every cent of your money goes / For cherries - in Butte - Montana. // There are buildings tall and buildings small, / Out there in Butte - Montana, / And they have buffets one and all, / 'Way out in butte - Montana; / Though it seldom rains it is safe to say / That you'll see rainbows every day, / And you hardly notice what you pay / For them - in Butte - Montana. // There's not a man who doesn't "live," / 'Way out in Butte - Montana, / And though his pocket-book's a sieve / He loves his Butte--Montana; / The wooley burg gets lots of knocks, / But just you get me off the rocks / And the laundry which next sees my socks / Will be in Butte - Montana!

- Souvenir, Annual Entertainment, Press Club of America, Metropolitan Opera House, Friday, May 6, 1904, The Press Club of Minneapolis, 1904, p 45; poem reprinted in McClure, Alexander Kelly: *Bohemia: A Symposium of Literary and Artistic Expressions by Men and Women Distinguished in Journalism, Art, Romance, Literature, Finance, Diplomacy, Politics, and Statecraft,* International League of Press Clubs, Philadelphia. 1904, p 227

There was a young fellow named Cain, / Who was wicked like Mary Mac-Lane. / With the leg of a table, / He slugged brother Abel, / And shouted, "Remember the Maine."
    - Vaugh, Stanton (ed.): *Limerick Lyrics: A Collection of Over 700 Choice Versifications, To Which is Added a Number of Short Verses, from Many Sources,* T.J. Carey & Co., New York, 1904, p 94

Mary MacLane is in Massachusetts, thinking again. - Harper's Weekly.
    On her vacation?
    - *Life,* 14 Sep 1905, p 313

Butte and Montana Beneath the X-Ray
No one seems to know what our Mary is doing. Perhaps she is spending her mornings and evenings in the Massachusetts hay gardens picking milk. - front title page

*

Miss Mary MacLane - Boston, Mass. -
    Why don't you come home, dearie? It is now nearly seven years since you used to take those long strolls out upon Butte's "sand and barrenness," flop down on the flat of your back, etc., so vividly described in your famous book, "The Story of Mary MacLane."
    For months and months after you left Butte for Massachusetts I poured out all the wealth of my pure affection upon you, my spirituelle creature.
    I titillated your intellectual appetite with honied phrases, coaxed you from the paths of folly with sugar plums and red ears of corn, gorged you with the milk of human kindness and well nigh pumped myself dry painting the lily, gilding refined gold and showering perfume on the violets for tootsy-wootsy.
    I was patient, long-suffering and gentle with you, Mary, but you sickened of my yum-yum and jumped the game. "Oh, gee, be sweet to me, kid." Can it be possible that some mischievous Puck has poured some accursed decoction into your soulful eyes - fair Titania - causing you to dote upon some Massachusetts ass mistaking his elephantine ears for angels' wings?

'Tis true? Ye Gods! Ye Gods! Ye pitying Gods! My heart is broken quite - the ruddy drops run down incarnadining all my lumbar region. Woe, woe, is me. There is no longer sun, nor stars, nor sea, the very flowers have lost their fragrance and wine its flavor, while all the spheres that in their jocund course did hymn celestial harmony do not breed discord dire. Is it any wonder that such cruel stabs have slit my cardiac pericardium from A to Izzard, spouting forth my bright red blood, even as the overloaded bombard spills his booze.

It cannot, cannot, be that my Mary, the paragon of gentleness and avatar of purity, known all over Montana as the X-Ray man's sweetheart[,] has quit him forever - some serpent having succeeded in poisoning our Hymenic Eden with its anguineal slime. 'Tis not like Mary of the gentle heart. Not thus did Cleopatra chide her Antony, nor Juliet roast her panting Romeo. 'Tis true, fair love, you and I used to have our little tiffs, for true love is ever a rocky road.

Beautiful damsel, sweet patron of love and wisdom who were wont to monkey with Minerva's owl and tangle your taper fingers in Aphrodite's shining hair, by remaining in silence in Massachusetts, the abiding place of the blooming bigot and the home of the crinose crank, by Heaven, I swear you do me wrong. Hast thou forgotten the old days in Butte, when playing Heloise to my Abelard, you would pout and pout until I would contract the sulks ?

Sometimes when I would write you gentle sonnets in which I ever called you Laura and signed myself Petrarch, you would complain that my muse was cold, Pegasus a mere plug, and hint that you would rather I would rush you against Newbro's ice cream joint or feed you on caramels, than sing your charms in Hudibrastic verse, but as a rule our lives ran on as smooth as oil on a summer sea.

Oftimes, on a Sunday afternoon, we would sail over to Pipestone Springs in one of Lavelle's rigs and there I watched you bathe your trilbies and tangle your taper fingers in the mountain brooks. After hitting all the roadhouses on the way home, indulging in a few races with other lovers out for a lark, dost remember your wish to be taken to Whatley's cafe, steered against the lone oyster in the soup and have your corset stuffed with chili con-carni and caviar lunches, instead of indulging in the usual program followed by lovers - that of letting me take you home and in the front parlor paw over the family album, finally winding up the evening's pleasure sitting on the sofa trying to swallow each other? Oh, Mary, "to dote, yet doubt; suspect yet strongly love." Will the green-eyed monster yet cause me to play the part of the o'er hasty Othello and journeying to Boston swat with a [hen] feather pillow the chaste janitress of my affections? Heaven forbid! Nit!

Up Eros! down Mars! Mary, you are all right. Your tongue may be a trifle shrewish but when it comes to a low-down it will be found that you are still my Annie, I'm your Joe and that all who are waiting to see me beat my resounding brisket and make moan like a he-Anemone, [of?] many fountained Ida, might just as well fall off the [k?]nee.

Come back to old Montana, Mary, you have spent seven years in the east hunting for your Devil. Break away from the vicinity of Boston, where there are 50,000 old maid century plants who want to get married and can't - where the men have to take to the storm cellars during leap year for protection.

Get out of Massachusetts, the land of professional pharisism, poke spectacles, flat bosoms and cold feet.

Come if you have to walk out of Boston bound for Montana, the home of the modern beauty, keeping time on the ties to the tune of

"Some airy nymph with fluent limbs / Through the dance luxuriant swims / Waving in her snowy hand / The leafy Bacchanalian wand."

"Hand" and "wand" don't rhyme very well, Mary, but editors like saloons, must have lots of "license." If on arriving back in dear old Butte, after seven years' absence, your editor sweetheart looks no longer good to you, there are 40 or 50 other unmarried men in Butte not under the care of the State Medical Institute among whom there would be some who can be trusted to carry in the coal and come home reasonably sober.

Hie you back to old Montana, the land of variety dives, enameled high kickers and expert beer canners. Bead carefully each issue of the X-Ray and it will eventually goad you into a Hymenic Elysium instead of leaving you alone and lorn with none to cuddle you to a manly brisket, praise your wondrous beauty, etc. Instead of being condemned to the comfortless companionship of tabby cats and poll parrots, you can buckle up in double harness with some big husky miner and soon see your sons smoking cigarettes, voting the democratic ticket and making an occasional sneak down to Arkansas Hot Springs, your female descendants chasing the bubble fame on pneumatic tires out towards the nine-mile house to meet some other woman's husband.

It is never too late to mend. "Hope springs eternal in the human breast." Old Neptune's steeds with their snowy manes along Boston Bay will never bring you your Devil. Come to Montana where there are plenty of Teddy bears and you will yet be happy. Yes, to old Montana, fair but neglected little cockle burr, where you can sit beneath the immediate drippings of the X-Ray and let it thaw you out. A few months' residence on your native heath and you will cease to relish the droning sermons of Massachusetts' one-idea preachers, the story of the worm fricasseed in the everlasting fire and the awful atrocities of the children of Israel. The Big Hole river water will work out your little liver, cleanse your blood, sweeten your breath and transform you into a thing of beauty and joy forever. Then you will relish your X-Ray and send your Warren bouquets of sweet buttercups and blue forget-me- nots. "Let the past be past" and hie you hither where copper is king and the Irish are cocks of the walk and bulls of the woods, where we go broke playing the races, drink at the fountain of perpetual youth and talk only of love and love's rapture - with other men's wives and other women's husbands - instead of moping in dark corners with atribilarious livers and scandalizing our neighbors.

As Troilus stood 'pon Ilion's ramparts and sighed his soul out toward the Grecian camp, where his fair Cressid was flirting with some other fellow, so stands your old sweetheart upon the sun-kissed pinnacle of Anaconda hill and calls upon his Mary to come out of the Massachusetts cold and take unto herself a Montana Apollo. Come, birdie, come home.

Lovingly,
Warren

(pp 13-16)

*

The West Side Literary Club of Butte, which includes a number of leading lady literati of the city, will hold sessions of the club once every two weeks during the coming winter. They announce nights with Shakespeare, Byron, Milton, Carlyle, Burns, Kipling, Ella Wheeler Wilcox, Mary MacLane and many others of past and present day fame. Owing to some oversight upon the part of the program committee they seem to have omitted a Night with Heinze which, in view of many events in Butte's history the past fifteen years, should certainly draw a full attendance of members qualified to speak on the subject. Collections will be taken at each meeting for the benefit of the suffering stockholders of the Anheuser-Busch Brewing Association. (p 22)

*

Butte's millionaire high society and its attaches and hangerson [*sic*] is infamy incarnate. It is worse than that. It is a hell boiled down to half a pint. Lawson and Mary MacLane have frequently tried to describe social conditions in Butte, but as there are depths in the ocean to which a stone will not sink, so is there depravity in Butte so fathomless that it is beyond the ability of mortal tongue to describe it. Drunkenness and about every other form of hideous debauchery known to infamy is altogether too commonplace in Butte's high society. And the worst feature of it is that a general knowledge of these things is not incompatible with social leadership. (p 153)

*

Senator Clark and Heinze and Buckets and Jack Munroe and two Bit Billie and Mary MacLane and Mickey the Greek and Gladys and Callihan the Bum and Stanley Ketchel and the editor of the X-Ray have all played their part in the upbuilding of the state of Montana and in giving it a name and fame throughout the world, but there is one that stands in a class all to himself. Twenty-five years ago, Charles M. Russell was an unknown range rider. Today he is the most famous artist of his kind in the world. He is known as the "cowboy artist." (pp 164-165)

*

Say, Mary Mac Lane, if it takes one of your flat-bosomed, cold-footed, poke spectacled Boston old maids beneath a Merry Widow hat an hour and a half to lick up a dish of ice cream with a hat pin, how much time should be allotted a crummy Montana lumberjack to pick the live stock off of himself with a pair of boxing gloves? (p 345)

*

With apologies to Mary McLane

From being a 90 pound man swinging a 300 pound woman across a ball room floor on a hot summer's night and feeling both suspender buttons give away behind; from picking a wife out of the A.B.C.; from prohibitionists, kind devil, deliver me. From the hotboxes in the Butte mines; from people who feel sorry for Heinze; from attending the average session of the Montana legislature, kind devil, deliver me. From the grafting of 15.00 per month per head in the Butte mines; from going through another copper war; from trying to run an automobile from the Nine Mile House up to Homestake, kind devil, deliver me, toodle-de-umpty-ido. (pp 355-356)

- Davenport, Warren G.: *Butte and Montana Beneath The X-Ray*, X-ray Pub. Co., Butte [Montana], 1908; C.F. Casenove, London, 1908; M. Galignani, Paris, 1909.

Literary Beginnings
Being Selected First Lines of Some Forthcoming Best Sellers
"Oh, hell," growled the Yukon Yap, "I'll get you for that!" - The He-Wolf's Fang, by Jack London

"Bertie Vanknickerhyde, descending the onyx, gold-inlaid steps of the Millionaires' Club, paused to light his famous pipe, carved from the Black Pearl of Samarcand, with a P.&R. bond of ten-thousand-dollar denomination." - The Chimpanzee-Toasters, by Upton Sinclair

"It is wholly (I use the word advisedly with due regard to the full force of its etymology) a matter of conjecture whether Aline Allingham, having looked into the inmost, hidden, subventricular recesses of her heart - a heart which no one could have called unduly susceptible to amatory, exclamatory phases - phases which are and will ever be." &c. - A Lady's Tintype, by Henry James

"Whoop - whoopee - listen to me - I quiver - I tremble - I've got 'em again." - Pyrotechnics of Mary MacLane

- *New York Times*, 10 Jul 1910, p SM5

Citations

"With the cry of a tigress she burned Lord Derringforth with her violet eyes." - Whose Heart?: Libbey.

"He pressed her ruby lips to his, the subtle incense from her raven hair setting his blood a-tingle." - Beverley of the Balkans: McCutcheon.

"I shriek. I snarl. I am a lioness; a she-cat; a leopardess of Numidia." - The Scream of Mary MacLane.

- *Life*, 27 Oct 1910, p 698

Montana
by George Fitch, Author of "At Good Old Siwash"

Montana is full of silver and gold, and the early settlers kept extremely busy getting it out and trading it for railroads and senatorships. There are few cities in Montana, and most of these are infested with smelters. A smelter is a small cross section of Hades in full operation. Only human beings will live in Butte and Anaconda. Trees, grass and flies have too much sense....

Montana has many unique attractions, including a large flock of glaciers, a herd of buffaloes, the largest chimney in the world, most of the remaining free and unlimited cowboys, the retortful Senator Dixon and Mary MacLane, who once wrote up Butte so vividly that many people still see it when they have been indulging in frenzied feeding.

- *Daily Commonwealth* [Fond du Lac, Wisconsin], 11 Jul 1912, p 4

Grand Divisions

Montana: A Northwestern copper mining property, once purchased by certain candidates for the United States Senate, but since permitted to revert to the government. Butte, the chief city, is the home of Mary MacLane, author of those inter-mountain classics, "Ooh-ooh-ooh!" and "I scream!"

The American Mineralogy

Copper: A mineral much employed in frenzied finance for the inauguration of panics. Found mainly around Butte, Montana, where the smelting fumes have killed off the vegetation and driven Mary MacLane into volume after volume of paroxysms and exclamation points.

- Stone, Stuart B[asham]: *The Nonsensical U.S.A.*, H.M. Caldwell Co., New York, 1912, pp 11, 17

Andrew's Leading Lady
by James Forbes

"Oh, you crave excitement!"
"Isn't it possible for a country girl to be ambitious?"
"Yes. There's Mary McLane."
"You refuse to consider me seriously."
- *The Speaker*, c. Jun 1913, p 172

The Missouri Convention - Tendencies and Hopes
by J.C. Kelsey

How easy it is to talk all day to each of you, individually. Yet when it comes to standing before you collectively, courage oozes out and thoughts skip quickly away through the feet. It really is sort of an imposition for a writer to talk to you, because you have to listen to him once a week, or once a month, as it happens to be. You do not have to read what I say. but if there is anything in the perseverance theory, you can't get away from me. You have me 32 times a year, as regularly as the sun shines. I sometimes feel that you believe in Mary MacLane to the extent of saying: "Kind Devil, deliver me from Kelsey!"
- *Telephony*, 14 Dec 1914, p 22

Conversations With "Con"
by The Invader

Butte, March 7

Mr. Editer, The Daily Meloussian:
... "Montana am great state," con ruminate, answerly in reply. "Montana's resources am the limit. Montana hav produce Charley Warren, Jack Monroe, Mary MacLane and Dick Kilroy."
- *Daily Missoulian* [Montana], 8 Mar 1914, p 4

Mary Maclane [*sic*] has broken loose again. "Of all living creatures that I know I most hate cockroaches," she says. Archy is not a revengeful person, but it is too much to be expected that he could overlook that. "Of all living creatures that I hate." said Archy when it was shown to him, "the majority are Human Beings!"

- Don Marquis

- *Washington Times* [Washington D.C.], 20 Apr 1917, p 8

A Line O' Type or Two
by B.L.T. [Bert Leston Taylor]
Literary Criticism in Milwaukee (from the Evening Wisconsin)

Mary MacLane has emerged from a period of quietude following an attempt to sustain with efflorescent originality the literary reputation she won with a flash on the appearance of her maiden effort, "Ships that Pass in the Night."
- *Chicago Daily Tribune*, 15 Jun 1917, p 8

Right off the Reel
As Mary MacLane Would Say - by Mae Tinee

I have a confession to make and it belongs in this column because it is the confession of a motion picture actor who believed, alas, that she had the soul of an artist.

The other night after reading late I became conscious of the gnawing of hunger, I looked frantically about for a box of candy. Some raiding hand however, had found the box before me and my fingers closed on nothingness.

"Well, the pantry for mine," I said. I gathered my draperies about me and went kitchenward.

The pantry was empty! There wasn't so much as a cracker or cookie there. The last of the cake had been eaten for dinner and hungry as I was I didn't feel like a can of corn.

"Ha," thought I, "the icebox! There will surely be something in the icebox!" There was. Some ice and a cold boiled potato!

I looked at the cold boiled potato and it seemed to look back at me with watery and understanding eyes. It seemed to say: "Ah, were you but I, Mary MacLane, your heart would leap for joy at sight of me. How tenderly you would gather me up and make me one with yourself! And as we became one, how you would thrill from palate to pedals!" All of this the cold boiled potato seemed to be saying to me as I looked at it and it appeared to look at me.

"Well," I said aloud, "I am an artist and here is artists' food. A cold boiled potato! The gods be good to myself and I and Mary MacLane. I will eat this cold, boiled potato and know the joy of perfect gastric satisfaction."

I took the cold boiled potato and drew it towards my lips. It had a strange and neutral odor. "Ah," quoth I to myself, "what is a cold boiled potato without salt," as I, Mary MacLane, would say. "A little salt, garcon!" Then I bit delicately into the anatomy of the cold boiled potato whereof I had salted. It tasted funny.

A little pepper, perhaps, is all that it would need. Perhaps it would make me feel like I, Mary MacLane! So, I put on a little pepper. Delicately I bit into the now salted and peppered cold boiled potato. It tasted funnier than ever!

To make a long story short I may inform you that I left nothing undone to that cold boiled potato. I buttered it I paprikaed it, I sprinkled it with a little vinegar, and finding a piece of parsley, I garnished it, but - here's the confession: I couldn't eat that cold boiled potato! I couldn't eat the DARN cold potato!
- *Chicago Daily Tribune*, 30 Sep 1917, p C3

Nutty Novelettes
The Worn Out Toothbrush - by Berton Braley
(With Apologies to Mary MacLane) [Illus. cartoon]

(1)

There is great tragedy in a worn out tooth brush. Its tired bristles remind me of my Western lover, who always wore a three days' beard. He was a high red blooded man, who had no time for all the ultra refinements of civilization. Aside from the bristles, there is nothing about the brush to remind me of my stalwart Western lover, for he never used a tooth brush.

(2)

I hang my worn out tooth brush above my dressing table and worship it at twilight. What could make a better idol than an idle tooth brush? I make it burnt offerings of cigarette butts and waste hair. The hair has a smell which is unbeautiful, cut so is the tooth brush. There is much beauty in the unbeautiful if you know how to look for it.

(3)

The back of my worn out tooth brush has a color like old ivory. It is not ivory, it is bone. But how often are bone and ivory one and the same. Consider Heinie Zimmerman.

(4)

As I contemplate my old worn out tooth brush I dream dreams. I dream of the succulent porker from which the bristles came, and my mouth waters until I go down into the ice box and dig a cold friend pork chop. How delicate is a cold friend pork chop at midnight!

(5)

You may ask me why I choose a worn out tooth brush as a subject. But I shall not answer. My Western lover, whose harsh bristles made my cheeks an ecstatically raw and passionately sore surface, did not understand it, either. But I gave him up rather than to give up my worn out tooth brush.

(6)

Sometimes I feel wild and angry with my tooth brush and decide to break it in my strong, beautiful hands - my hands that I often sit and hold in each other for hours because I love them so. But I do not break the tooth brush.

Perhaps when I have written 20,000 more words about it I shall cast it away and get a new one, but I shall await my royalty statements first. For I might not have enough money to buy a new one.

(7)

If I were a painter I should paint my worn out tooth brush, swinging on the nail above my table. And the painting should have all the pathos, the exhaustion, the terror, the ugliness, and the beauty of the brush - but never the usefulness of it. For you cannot wash your teeth with a painting.

- *Salt Lake Telegram* [Utah], 29 Dec 1917, p 7

Diary Of Our Own Samuel Pepys
[by F.P.A. (Franklin Pierce Adams)]

27th January: ... After breakfast, I did read from the book "I Mary MacLane," which is not exceeded in ego by even the author of "Alone in Cuba." But while Mary explores the secret motives of her inmost thoughts, Teddy explored Africa and Panama and Standard Oil and other obnoxious things and telleth in boastful language how he came and saw and conquered. But a little of Mary goeth a long way and so I turn to a book by Jack London and read "When the Earth Was Young," albeit I am doubtful of Jack being there at the time.

- *Des Moines News* [Iowa], 28 Jan 1918, p 4

In the Wake of the News
By Ring W. Lardner [Illus. cartoon]

Yesterday

It's a Tuesday morning and I'd amazingly love to eat a Cold Boiled Prune.

I shall never be able to tell one-tenth of my quaintly-vulgar Tuesday morning fondness for a Cold Boiled Prune.

But now I must work, work, work, work, work. So I write me this stuff of me.

I find Me in this Chicago-Illinois, in a sweetly Madison street picture-show. I am fascinatingly-B.&O'ly late. The things I see are garbledly-tangled into an indescribable heap in my abdomen. I can write of them only vaguely-jumbley.

*

The picture is You, Mary MacLane, and your Passionate Male Sextet.

I see your white flannel-trouseredly naughty boy.

And I see your portfolioly pen-pushing black-black-black bow-tied writer-man.

And your too easily ossified son-of-baronet.

And your napkin-in-his-necked box fighter.

And your anti-alcoholic bucolic bank clerk.

And your married devil-in-his own-home-town.

I see all six of the Men Who Have Made Love to You (and by the way, Mary, I'll say you weren't entirely on the defensive).

And I hear them and others subtitley addressing you with such remarks as "Say listen" and "I should worry" and "You're some jane" and "For God's sake, lay off him". And I see you standing for it.

*

And I must admit that even if you do play with a doll and drink cocktails and don a kimono at 7:50 P.M., I'm off'n You, Mary MacLane, and never again will I believe that a girl is damnably different because of what she says in a book.

You're a broken idol with I, Ring Lardner, and in spite of my futile way-of-life and my rotting destroying half acquiescence in it I have a furious positive Murder in me.

I do not know why I don't do the Murder. It is not from fear of consequences - not in this Chicago-Illinois.

It would be simpler and finer for me to do this Murder than to keep it in me.

It would be a simpler and fine thing to do any Murder than to feel even once, the strangling damnedness rising, rising at my throat.

I wish I'd been born a Wild Boar.

- *Chicago Daily Tribune,* 12 Feb 1918, p 14

In the Wake of the News
The Epistles of Edna - By Ring W. Lardner

Chicago, July 4

Dear Mr. Graves: Well, you see I have enclosed the photo and now it's "up to you." Isn't this a crazy one of me? I had no idea my girl friend was going to take my picture and I am afraid I look like the "Last Rose of summer" in it or something. It was taken a year ago when a girl friend and myself were spending our vacation up at South Haven. I bet you will say it's a wonder I didn't break the camera. But you know you asked me for a photo and this is the only one I have so "anything to oblige." But don't forget you promised to exchange with me and if you don't send me one of yourself right away I will know you are a "gay deceiver." ...

Did I tell you what I was reading today? It was "I, Mary MacLane" and I guess it must have been about the "steenth" time I have read it. What a wonderful mind she has and how she simply fascinates a person. Sometimes I think I will write a book like her's and just set my thoughts down as they come, but I'm afraid the whole book would be just one person's name written over and over again, only I would have to know their first name before I could write it.

You will think I am a crazy little "it" if I keep on so I will close. Remember the photo and also that I am not Miss Conklin but just

Your (?) Edna

- *Chicago Tribune*, 7 Jul 1918, p A1

Oh, Don't You Remember Sweet Mary, Ben Bolt?

"What has become of Mary MacLane?" asks a reader. We don't know, at this moment, but we remember - what is more important - a jingle by the late lamented Roz Field: She dwelt beside the untrodden ways, / Among the hills of Butte, / A maid whom no one cared to love, / And no one dared to shoot.

- Taylor, Bert Leston: *The So-Called Human Race* (Henry B. Fuller, ed.), Alfred A. Knopf, New York, 1922, p 236

Roast Beef and Green Peas

My career as a public speaker is not yet ended. What the future will bring forth I do not know but, like Mary MacLane, I pray that Satan may deliver me from -

Chairmen who cannot pronounce my name,
Microphones that whistle or shriek,
People who want to sell me antiques,
Girls in the audience who giggle,
Roast beef, green peas, community singing, dancing children,
And, above all, may Satan deliver me from
My urge to write another unorthodox book on Lincoln.

- Eisenschiml, Otto: *Without Fame: The Romance of a Profession*, Alliance Book Corp., New York, 1942, pp 358-359

NEWSPAPER SQUIBS

Encouraging Mary

Mary MacLane needn't worry. Fame and prosperity are sure to be hers. The public libraries will soon begin barring out her book. - Chicago Record-Herald
- *Butte Inter Mountain* [Montana], 3 May 1902, p 4

While doing all they possibly can to spread the fame of their literary celebrity, Mary MacLane; none of the Butte newspapers has yet published a picture of the young lady in her favorite pose, feet on the bureau, "always on the bureau," although they have represented her in almost every other possible position. Such a picture printed over the announcement that her book has been refused a place on the shelves of Butte's public library should increase the sales of the young lady's compilation of sensuality and lustful desire, to an unheard of degree.
- *Billings Gazette* [Montana], 6 May 1902, p 4

The "Story of Mary MacLane" will not be admitted to the Butte public school library if the keeper of that institution has his say. It must be a hard proposition.
- *Fergus County Argus* [Lewistown, Montana], 7 May 1902, p 4

Miss Mary MacLane has at least succeeded in writing a book that is strenuous enough to do its own advertising.
- *Washington Post*, 9 May 1902, p 6

Too Much of a Good Thing

It is reported that Mary MacLane intends to move to Chicago. Hold on, Mary! Don't come just as the hot weather is settling in. - Chicago Record-Herald
- *Butte Inter Mountain* [Montana], 10 May 1902, p 4, col. 2

Our Mary

There was a young woman of Butte, / Who said to herself: "I'll be cute. / So she wrote naughty things, / Fame arrived on swift wings, / And she chuckled: "Oh ain't I a beaut?" - Chicago Record-Herald
- *Butte Inter Mountain* [Montana], 10 May 1902, p 4, col. 3

Mary MacLane will be sure to produce a loud demand for the literary disinfectants.
- *Washington Post*, 12 May 1902, p 6

Mary McLane is merely a female faddist.
- *Des Moines Capital* [Iowa], 14 May 1902, p 4

Silver Bow county has no debt but it has Mary MacLane.
- *Fergus County Argus* [Lewistown, Montana], 14 May 1902, p 4

Mount Pelee belongs to the Mary MacLane class of volcanoes.
- *Fergus County Argus* [Lewistown, Montana], 14 May 1902, p 4

Our Mary
Poisoned Shafts of Envy Shot from Other Towns
St. Paul Globe - Mary MacLane, the Montana girl who declares her love for the devil, is probably booked for just about that sort of a time.

Minneapolis Journal - She acts and writes like a composite of Calamity Jane, Maria Hicks and the Cherry Sisters.

Milwaukee Sentinel - Mary MacLane's book is pronounced not fit to read. Its success now seems assured.
- *Butte Inter Mountain* [Montana], 15 May 1902, p 4

Some enterprising firm should hasten to place some "Mary McLane Dyspepsia Pellets" on the market.
- *Des Moines Capital* [Iowa], 15 May 2014, p 4

The impression that Mary MacLane is a horrid man continues to take root.
- *Washington Post*, 23 May 1902, p 6

Current Press Comment
Mary had a little bug - / She thought that She was It. / She wrote a book of shocking things / And straightway made a hit. - Buffalo Express
- *Washington Times* [Washington, D.C.], 27 May 1902, p 6

Mary MacLane, the forlorn maiden who awaits the coming of her devil, and indifferently rakes in 15 cents every time one of her books disappears in the maw of a hungry public! Think of it! 100,000 books times 15 cents; 100,000 drinks! - Dupuyer Acantha [Montana]
- *Butte Inter Mountain* [Montana], 28 May 1902, p 4

It is very strange that while the season is on we have had no eruption from the upper end of Nikola Tesla. Is he also extinct?
- *Atlanta Constitution*, 29 May 1902, p 6

Mary MacLane is about to erupt again and the literary embalmers will have another strong subject on their hands.
- *Atlanta Constitution*, 29 May 1902, p 6

Will some one please pass Miss Mary MacLane a piece of the red, red sky she is starving for, also a small bottle of tabasco sauce to flavor it with. - Montana Record
  - *Ogden Standard* [Utah], 29 May 1902, p 4

Mangled in a Mergenthaler
And still the people keep on buying Mary McLane's wicked little book.
- *Saint Paul Globe* [Minnesota], 1 Jun 1902, p 4

Montana saloon keepers are serving what they call the "Mary MacLane highball." It is described as something fierce.
- *Chicago Daily Tribune*, 2 Jun 1902, p 12

The Mary McLane book is no better than scores of others which have come from the press during the past two years - nor can it be said that it is much worse. Of course, if the latter truth gets out it will spoil sales.
- *Virginia Enterprise* [St. Louis County, Minnesota], 6 Jun 1902, p 2

Preparing to Examine It
Young author: "I have here a dramatization of the "Story of Mary MacLane."
  Manager (to office boy): "Johnny, run out and get 15 cents worth of chloride of lime." - Chicago Record-Herald
  - *St. Louis Republic*, 7 Jun 1902, Pt I, p 6

The new Mary MacLane cigar will probably smoke up like a house afire.
- *Red Lodge Picket* [Montana], 4 Jul 1902, p 4

Disbrow, charged with murder, is receiving love letters from young women who know him only through the newspapers. This spoils Mary MacLane's record as the champion silly girl.
- *Evening Star* [Washington, D.C.], 8 Jul 1902, p 4

Along The Kansas Nile
Kansas doesn't produce all the western freaks. We are not responsible for Mary McLane.
- *Wichita Daily Eagle* [Kansas], 9 Jul 1902, p 4

Mary MacLane gives us a pain. / She comes from Butte, / Where bad men shutte - and then -- our poet fainted.
- *Chicago Livestock World*, 10 Jul 1902, p 4

By giving Mary MacLane a thorough college course they will doubtless be able to extract all the originality from the lady's mind.
- *Washington Post*, 11 Jul 1902, p 6

Only Mary MacLane could do justice to such weather.
- *Bluefield Daily Telegraph* [West Virginia], 12 July 1902, p unknown

Pulse of the Press
The Story of Mary MacLane is 100 in the shade. - Memphis Morning News
- *Enterprise-Register* [Palatine, Illinois], 12 Jul 1902, p 10

A 5-cent cigar has been named for Mary MacLane. The purchasers of this particular weed will have to place the lighted end in their mouths in order to get the full benefit of the nomenclature.
- *Washington Post*, 12 Jul 1902, p 6

Mary MacLane is going east to get educated and, we trust, fumigated.
- *Atlanta Constitution*, 13 Jul 1902, p 24

It is claimed that the net earnings of some of the big mining properties near Butte, Mont. show a decrease of nearly $10,000,000 this year as compared with last season. This will help to offset the rapidly increasing royalties on that bad book by Mary MacLane.
- *Daily Northwestern* [Oshkosh, Wisconsin], 14 Jul 1902, p 4

Some one has named a cigar after Mary MacLane. It emits a blue flame and sulphurous smoke. - St. Paul Globe
- *Amsterdam Evening Recorder* [New York], 15 Jul 1902, p 8

A cigar has been named after Mary MacLane and those who use it have to plagiarize her tooth brush oaths.
- *Atlanta Constitution*, 16 Jul 1902, p 6

Mary Maclane [*sic*.], who is in Chicago, in quest of her devil, says the Windy City doesn't interest her. Mary might try Mt Clemens, Mich. Mary will find old Meph. there all right, leading a strenuous life.
- *Marion Daily Star* [Ohio], 16 July 1902, p 4

Today's Topics
Mary MacLane will be in Buffalo today. Why? The Man Devil does not live here.
- *Buffalo Express* [New York], 17 Jul 1902, p 1

The West is very much excited over the Eastern triumphal literary progress of Miss Mary MacLane. Hence the "Limerick:" There was a young woman of Butte, / A wild; woolly Western galoot, / She said, Damn ! damn damn / I'm a genius, I am " / And Chicago said, "Isn't she cute?" - New York Sun
- *Butte Inter Mountain* [Montana], 17 Jul, 1902, p 4

Mary MacLane now says that she has decided that she is not a genius. If this is a correct report the person who brought her to that conviction is one.
- *Bluefield Daily Telegraph* [West Virginia], 19 Jul 1902, p unknown

That eastern elite college flatly refuses to take Mary MacLane for a pupil. The faculty probably thinks Mary needs to unlearn a lot of things before taking on a further curriculum.
- *Atlanta Constitution*, 21 Jul 1902, p 4

Now Mary Maclane is lost somewhere between Buffalo and Boston. That destroys our illusion that Mollie is one of those girls that you can't lose.
- *Atlanta Constitution*, 22 Jul 1902, p unknown

So Mary MacLane can't enter Radcliffe College, eh? Doesn't Radcliffe recognise a genius even when it is labeled by the first person singular?
- *Buffalo Express* [New York], 23 Jul 1902, p 6

Mary MacLane now says that by "man devil" she meant only ideal man and that the term she used was selected merely to avoid a hackneyed phrase. Mary is becoming conventional fast since she left Butte.
- *Buffalo Express* [New York], 23 Jul 1902, p 6

Contrary to expectation Boston does not appear to have chilled Mary Mac-Lane.
- *Bluefield Daily Telegraph* [West Virginia], 25 Jul 1902, p unknown

The eastern preacher who announces that the devil is "handsome and captivating" seems to agree very well with the opinion of Mary MacLane.
- *Daily Northwestern* [Oshkosh, Wisconsin], 25 Jul 1902, p 4

Unappreciated
In Tolstoi's latest book the Russian pessimist asserts that English fiction died with Dickens and American literature ceased with Emerson and Lowell. This is tough on Samuel Eberly Gross and Mary McLane. - Philadelphia Press
- *Rochester Democrat & Chronicle* [New York], 25 July 1902, p 6

Mary MacLane's discussion of the problems of life is just as reckless as if she were a professor in the University of Chicago.
- *Virginia Enterprise* [St. Louis County, Minnesota], 25 Jul 1902, p 6

Can it be possible that nobody is going to dramatize Mary MacLane?
- *Manti Messenger* [Utah], 26 Jul 1902, p 4

Mary MacLane indignantly denies that she has invaded the east for the purpose of being reformed.
- *Daily Northwestern* [Oshkosh, Wisconsin], 1 Aug 1902, p 4

The Comic Side of the News
Mary MacLane does not read all that is printed abut her. The poor girl has to have some sleep.
- *Enterprise-Register* [Palatine, Illinois], 2 Aug 1902, p 2

If the papa of Mary MacLane / Would purchase a good heavy cane, / And call her one side, / And warm up her hide, / She'd never say d___n d___n, again.
- *Goodwin's Weekly* ("A thinking paper for thinking people") [Salt Lake City, Utah], 2 Aug 1902, p 5

What if Mary MacLane should decide to go on the stage?
- *Coshocton Daily Age* [Ohio], 4 Aug 1902, p unknown

The Comic Side of the News
Mary MacLane does not read all that is printed about her. The poor girl has

to have some sleep.
- *Dakota Farmers' Leader* [Canton, South Dakota], 8 Aug 1902, p 2

Mary McLane, the strenuous authoress of the west[,] has gone up against Boston. The beaneaters warmed up to Oscar Wilde more than they did to the prairie girl. Mary will have to trail back to Butte to again be perfectly happy.
- *Red Lodge Picket* [Montana], 8 Aug 1902, p 4

Mary MacLane's "calm, beautiful stomach" must have stopped its singing and used her famous word "damn" on Monday morning when she unloaded upon it the following "New England breakfast": Baited beans, pickles, maple syrup, doughnuts, coffee, fish balls, blueberries and biscuits. - Boston Herald
- *Goodwin's Weekly* [Salt Lake City, Utah], 9 Aug 1902, p 26

Mary MacLane is writing another heart romance, compared to which her maiden effort will seem like a cold-storage tamale.
- *New Era* [Humeston, Iowa], 13 Aug 1902, p 6

The chances are that the devil would have nothing to do with Mary MacLane. Mary is too fresh for the devil.
- *Wichita Daily Eagle* [Kansas], 17 Aug 1902, edit. sect., p 18

The Nonpareil Man
Mary MacLane says she saw a man in Chicago that she might love. We were passing through Chicago at that time, but it was on a Sunday. Besides, we had our fingers crossed.
- *Minneapolis Journal*, 19 Aug 1902, p 4

The Nonpareil Man
Grave old-Boston has turned out the first parody on Mary MacLane's book. It is called "The Story of Lizzie McGuire," and is exceptionally tiresome as all parodies are if they don't watch out.
- *Minneapolis Journal*, 20 Aug 1902, p 4

Mary MacLane's silence seems to indicate that she has met the devil and that she is "his'n."
- *Arizona Republican* [Phoenix], 3 Sep 1902, p 2

Mary MacLane says. "I was born to be alone." Poor Mary. She ought to have a "little lamb" at least.
- *Fergus County Argus* [Lewistown, Montana], 3 Sep 1902, p 4

Topics of the Times
Mary MacLane says, "I was born to be alone." It is plain from this that Mary plays upon the piano.
- *Hayward Review* [California], 10 Oct 1902, p 4

Mary McLane's arrest on suspicion of being a burglary [*sic*.] will give her fresh advertising and enable her to break into the coffers of book readers with another bid for notoriety.
- *Virginia Enterprise* [St. Louis County, Minnesota], 7 Nov 1902, p 7

Chicago has a Mary MacLane in the person of Viola Larsen, of extraordinary idiosyncrasies. This justifies the claim that you can get anything in Chicago which can be found anywhere on earth.
- *Marion Daily Star* [Ohio], 22 Nov 1902, p 4

The Nonpareil Man
Elsie Viola Larsen is trying to Mary-maclane herself somewhere. Particulars not in yet.
- *Minneapolis Journal*, 27 Nov 1902, p 4

A Chicago girl who claims to be a second Mary MacLane has been arrested. She should be severely punished. It was bad enough for one to have been a first Mary MacLane.
- *Washington Post*, 30 Nov 1902, p 18

Mary MacLane's book is to be published in England. The English are notoriously deficient in the art of swearing and are evidently going to take some steps to improve themselves in that line.
- *Fergus County Argus* [Lewiston, Montana], 3 Dec 1902, p 3

A Chicago girl has been arrested for trying to be a second Mary MacLane. Give the poor thing a guardian.
- *Humeston New Era* [Iowa], 17 Dec 1902, p 6

Woman's Column
Neway [sic.] Items to Interest the Fair Sex

Oh! say, what do you think? Mary MacLane has written a book and now there will be something to talk about in the line of hot stuff in literature.
- *Marcelus Weekly Observer* [New York], Mar 1903, p unknown

Help Wanted?

A. Fusser - What would you do if I should kiss you?

Mary McLane - I would scream for help.

A. Fusser - Why, don't you think I could do it alone? - Pennsylvania Punch Bowl
- *New York Sun*, 10 May 1903, p 11

Mary MacLane of Butte is going to write another book. That girl absolutely refuses to wash dishes and dust the parlor.
- *Evening Star* [Washington, D.C.], 2 Jul 1903, p 4

Mary MacLane announces from Butte that she is about to further expose her "naked soul." Well, Mary, if you will do it, weather conditions are favorable.
- *Atlanta Constitution*, 13 Jul 1903, p 4

Montana is now bracing herself for the impact of another book by Mary McLane. And it might be just as well for the rest of us to likewise stiffen our sinews a little.
- *Los Angeles Times*, 25 Jul 1903, p 6

Vesuvius is not the only volcano that is resuming business. The Western papers report that both Carrie Nation and Mary McLane are getting active again.
- *Times Dispatch* [Richmond, Virginia], 28 Jul 1903, p 4

Mary MacLane's new book is out, and is so disappointingly respectable that but little attention will probably be paid to it.
- *Washington Post*, 29 Jul 1903, p 6

It will also be noted that soon after Mary MacLane had her second eruption of literature it snowed in Butte.
- *Bismarck Daily Tribune*, 9 Sep 1903, p 2

Mary McLane thinks Boston is just too utterly too-too for any use, but Boston hasn't lorgnetted Mary long enough yet to say what it does think of her. - Atlanta Journal.
- *Semi-Weekly Messenger* [Wilmington, N.C.] 6 Oct 1903, p 2

Mary MacLane says the future is a lute without strings. It may also be described as an untooted flute.
- *Delphos Daily Herald* [Ohio], 2 Nov 1903, p unknown

A warning to eligible young devils: Mary MacLane announces that she is looking for a husband.
- *Marion Daily Star* [Ohio], 6 Nov 1903, p 4

Much to the disgust of the coal dealers, Mary MacLane has arrived in New York to spend the winter. The New Yorkers confidently believe that all danger of a severe winter is over.
- *Anaconda Standard* [Montana], 17 Nov 1903, p 6

Reflections of a Bachelor
If Mary McLane ever should happen to meet her affinity, there'll be a foot-race, with the famous Butte girl in pursuit.
- *Anamosa Prison Press* [Iowa], 14 May 1904, p 2

Sic transit gloria mundi. Some of the newspapers now spell it "Mary McLean;" others, "Mary McLane;" and still others, "Mary MacLane."
- *Saint Paul Globe* [Minnesota], 2 Aug 1904, p 4

Mary McLane went back to Butte to get some local color and was stricken with scarlet fever. We knew Mary would get too much some time.
- *Paducah Evening Sun* [Kentucky], 31 Jan 1910, p 4

With Heinze and Mary MacLane both located at Butte there is liable to be a beaut of a story from there soon.
- *Rock Island Argus* [Illinois], 27 May 1910, p 4

Mary MacLane says she is against a fat man for president. It takes a lean guy to make a hit with girls like Mary who carry pickles in their shirt waists. Despite our advantages in the matter of figure, however, we can't all be presidents.
- *Evening Telegram* [Elyria, Ohio], 2 Dec 1910, p 4

Fallen

O little comets tumble / From out their firmaments: / This morning, with a sense of pain, / I saw The "Story of Mary MacLean" / Marked down to twenty cents.

- *Rock Island Argus* [Illinois], 23 Apr 1913, p 4

The Press Gallery

The woman who tried to make a book out of herself, and called it, "I, Mary MacLane" eulogizes, among other things, her hat. "Take away my clothes," she says, "but leave me my hat, for it is a part of myself." Of course we are not going to do anything of the sort. But does she, one wonders, go to bed in it?

- *Binghampton Press* [New York], 21 May 1917, p 6

Mystery of Mysteries
(From Field's ad)

It is bad enough at best; but it is terrible as we read it in the Minneapolis Journal: "Mary MacLane in Men Who Have Made Love to Me, all week."

- *Evening State Journal & Lincoln Daily News* [Nebraska], 11 Feb 1918, p 6

Close-ups of Some of Film-land's Best Known Stars
by Bessie Willmore

Mary McLane is coming in the much talked of picture, "Men Who Have Made Love to Me." Elliot Dexter, Marie Doro's husband, seemed to take to the idea, for he's written an article on "Women I Have Loved." But his is the "reel" kind of love, while Mary's - well, see for yourself.

- *Fort Wayne News and Sentinel* [Indiana], 13 April 1918, p 4

NOTES

Given the number of quotations, paraphrases, echoes, etc. of MacLane in the newspaper items and the three books, the ed. does not provide orig. source refs. for her works; similarly, he only notes the reprinted texts' more interesting or obscure refs. and archaisms.

*

7. *Rediscovery* - The editor offers a summary chronology, regularly updated, at http://fuguewriter.wordpress.com/ (accessed 10 May 2013).

7. *I Await* - Unexpurgated text avail. in various vols. pub 2014, Petrarca Press, Austin [Texas], ed. Michael R. Brown: *Human Days: A Mary MacLane Reader*; *I Await the Devil's Coming - Annotated & Unexpurgated*; *Tender Darkness: A Mary MacLane Sampler*); expurgated text pub. 2013, Melville House, New York (*I Await the Devil's Coming*, intro. Jessa Crispin).

7. *doctoral dissertations* - *Autobiography, Genius, and the American West: The Story of Mary MacLane and Opal Whiteley* by Cathryn Luanne Halverson, University of Michigan, 1997 & *"The Unparalleled Individuality of Me": The Story of Mary MacLane* by Kathryne Beth Tovo, University of Texas at Austin, 2000.

7. *or invented* - Cf. *Human Days* (2014) p 569 n 264.

8. *Triggs* - Quoted in "Lauds Mary M'Lane Now - Prof. Triggs Praises the Butte Girl's Book," *Chicago Daily Tribune*, 27 June 1902, p 5.

8. *Darrow* - *Chicago American*, 4 May 1902. p unknown.

8. *Porter Garnett* - in "The Importance of the Unimportant and Other Phenomena," *Pacific Monthly - Vol. XVIII - July-Dec 1907*, Pacific Monthly Pub. Co., Portland [Or.], 1907, p 434.

8. *mere cheap* - Cf. her earliest known letter to her publisher (22 Apr 1902, in *Human Days* [2014], p 263); goes on to say cheap notice and sensation "can only detract from it. I think the best possible advertisement for it would be a severe criticism in the *Bookman* or *Book-buyer* or some equally well known reviewer."

11. *magazine editor* - Cf. *Book News*, Jun 1903, pp 786-787.

12. *bibliographic error* - Cf., e.g., Miller, Meredith: *Historical Dictionary of Lesbian Literature*, Scarecrow Press, Lanham (MaryLand), 2006, p 116 & Reginald, Robert et. al.: *Science Fiction and Fantasy Literature (Vol. I)*, Wildside Press LLC, 2010, p 616.

12. *By Himself* - As with *Willie* and *Lizzie*, a deliberate echo of *I Await*, which as *The Story* bore title-page explanation "By Herself."

12. *author information* - Cf. *Tender Darkness: A Mary MacLane Anthology*, ed. Elisabeth Pruitt, Abernathy & Brown, Belmont [Calif.], 1993, p 198.

12. *contemporaneous responses* - A book-length riposte to MacLane's final book is also by a woman: Gertrude Sanborn's *I, Citizen of Eternity: A Diary of Hopeful Days* (Four Seas Co., Boston, 1920 - title deliberate parallel to *I, Mary MacLane: A Diary of Human Days* [Frederick A. Stokes, New York, 1917].) Sanborn "attained some notice for her novel *Veiled Aristocrats* (1922), which dealt with race relations more directly than was fashionable at the time." - http://en.wikipedia.org/wiki/ Gertrude_Sanborn (accessed 10 May 2015)

12. *one-shot* - A company by that name (*sans* hypen) was active in the 1870s in Wisconsin and Kansas, but there was a very length interregnum and no evident connection between the two.

12. *a figure* - Cf., e.g., Redmond, Donald A.: *Sherlock Holmes Among the Pirates: Copyright and Conan Doyle in America*, Greenwood Press, Westport [Conn.], 1990, pp 61-63, 130, 203; Weber, Carl J.: *Hardy in America: A Study of Thomas Hardy and His American Readers*, Russell & Russell, New York, 1966, p 37; Eitel, Edmund Henry (ed.): *The Complete Works of James Whitcomb Riley*, Bobbs-Merrill, Indianapolis, 1913, p 445.

13. *pirate* - The editor has found 1890s Weeks eds. of Robert Louis Stevenson, Grant Allen, Anna Sewell, Ouida, and others.

13. *fraud* - Weeks is remembered today among art and book-printing specialists for, of all things, a fine eye in cover art. In 1987, the Metropolitan Museum of Art would cite him as possibly the first publisher to wrap books in poster-like covers, with art commissioned by the soon-to-be sensationally successful J.C. Leyendecker, who, the Museum recorded, did his first poster for Weeks *c.* 1895; *cf.* Kiehl, David W. and Cate, Phillip Dennis: *American Art Posters of the 1890s: In the Metropolitan Museum of Art, Including the Leonard A. Lauder Collection*, Metropolitan Museum of Art, New York, 1987, p 53. http://books.google.com/ books?id=to-pF5vd3VoC&pg=PA53#v=onepage&q&f=false (accessed 10 May 2015) shows a non-pirate 1898 Weeks novel: *Ionia: Land of Wise Men and Fair Women,* now considered an early science fiction work: blend of secret Himalayan society, airplanes, pollution control and recycling, eugenics, government ownership of land, eugenics, alternative energy, and anti-Semitism; public domain edition at http://books.google.com/books?id=dX_QAAAAMAAJ (accessed 10 May 2015); *cf.* http://en.wikipedia.org/wiki/Ionia_(novel) (accessed 10 May 2015).

13. *deigned* - *Cf. The American Catalog, 1900-1905*, Office of the Publisher's Weekly, New York, 1905, p 669; listing, doubtless drawn from Library of Congress information, discloses author's name as "Mrs. T.D. McKown."

13. *standing* - "Although the letters are written by 'Himself,' the publishers state that the author is 'a lady of high standing in social and literary circles.'" - *Bookseller, Newsdealer & Stationer*, 1 Jan 1904, p 17; *Brooklyn Daily Eagle*, 19 Jan 1904, p 13 repeats author's social standing without quotation and adds western USA location.

13. *in 1869* - *Cf.* 1900 census for Colorado, Teller County, Cripple Creek District 19, Ward 4, 9 June 1900, sheet 24, end; 1910 census for Georgia, Walker County, Lookout mountain Militia District, [*c.* 20] May 1910, sheet 24A.

13. *inventor* - *Cf., e.g.*, US patent no. 661,812, "Surgical Apparatus," filed 1900, cited in five US patents filed 1997-2012; US patent no. 898,773, "Shaving-Mug", filed 1907, cited in patent filed 1976.

13. *Chickamauga* - *Cf. Transactions of the Medical Association Georgia - Forty-Seventh Annual Session*, Medical Assoc. of Georgia, Atlanta, 1896, p 346 for Dr. McKown's location in 1887.

13. *1897* - *Cf. Colorado Medical Journal, Vol. III*, Colorado Medical Journal Publishing Co., Denver, 1897, p 256.

13. *apart from* - *Cf. Thirty-Second Annual Denver City Directory*, Ballenger & Richards, Denver, 1904, p 791.

13. *postmaster* - *Cf. National Archives Microfilm Publications - Record of Appointments of U. S. Postmasters, 1832-September 30, 1971*, Washington, 1973, p 868 (in orig. record at roll 25, Georgia, Quitman-Worth Counties).

13. *died* - Brief obit. in *Journal of the American Medical Association, Volume 63*, American Medical Assoc., Chicago, 1914, p 1493: "Thomas B. [*sic.*] McKown, M.D. Atlanta, Ga., Medical College, 1885; a Fellow of the American Medical Association; surgeon to the Durham Coal and Coke Company, Lookout Mountain Coal and Coke Company and Georgia Penitentiary; and a practitioner of Pittsburg, Ga.; died at the home of his mother in Jonesboro, Ga., September 24 [1914], aged 54." However, photo at http://www.findagrave.com/cgi-bin/fg.c gi?page=gr&GSln=MCK&GSpartial=1&GSbyrel=all&GSst=12&GScntry=4& GSsr=4641&GRid=36023260& (accessed 10 May 2015) shows headstone death date of 1917.

14. *125 active* - *Club Women of New York*, Mail & Express Co., New York, 1904, p 325.

14. *Fourth of* - Direct take-off of MacLane's account of Butte's Miner's Union Day: *I Await*, entry of 3 Feb 1902, in *Human Days* (2014) pp 51-54.

15. *first article* - MacLane, Mary: "A Foreground and a Background," *Denver Post*, 4 Oct 1903; in *Human Days* (2014) p 245-248.

15. *varnished* - It's worth noting that MacLane describes six characters in her Colorado Springs visit: a placid woman with an air of great profoundness; a woman tight, intellectual, and defensive about it; a plain, humorous woman who made many puns; a messy, light-hearted, happy person; a lady serene, quiet, carefully unobjectionable; a strenuous woman given to long speeches with such phrases as "general good," "work of the past year," and "dignity of the club women." McKown gives us six as well: a round-shouldered, intellectual woman with secret dreams of literary fame; the wordy chairperson of the philanthropy committee; an enthusiast who thinks *The Story* praiseworthy and wonderfully expressed; a philosophical lady who objects to MacLane's book on grounds of morals yet allows it has value; a harsh-voiced woman who says MacLane was motivated by desire for a man; and the fascinating Mrs. Gatewood. The composition of *Letters* appears to have been rapid: MacLane's Colorado visit was in October 1903; newspaper mentions of *Letters* begin by early December: *cf.* brief review, *St. Louis Republic*, 5 Dec 1903, Pt II, p 2, also excerpts in *Brooklyn Daily Eagle*, 19 Jan 1904, p 13; various newspapers (e.g., *San Francisco Call*, *Minneapolis Journal*) mention review copies received in Dec. 1903-Jan. 1904.

*

19. *Methodist ... Gruntgander* - If a ref., an untraceable one.

19. *the rains* - An unusual rendering of Matthew 7:25; compare King James: *And the rain descended, and the floods came, and the winds blew, and beat upon that house; and it fell not: for it was founded upon a rock*; only other appearances ed. has found is in *I Await*, entry of 20 March (*cf. Human Days* [2014], p 89), and in pamphlet "The Errors and Crimes of Prohibition" (interior title "Prohibition Founded on Falsehood," supertitled part of series "A Tract for the Times - No. 2") by Lovejoy, Joseph Cammet: [no publisher named], Boston, 1871, p 2.

20. *Margeurite* - Ref. to Gounod's *Faust*; name in Goethe's ver. is Gretchen/Margaret.

20. *and gnashing* - Matthew 13:42: *And shall cast them into a furnace of fire: there shall be wailing and gnashing of teeth.* (King James)

20. *neither death* - From Romans 8:38-39 (King James).

21. *with another* - MacLane's second book, *My Friend Annabel Lee*, was published on 1 September 1903; this would place McKown's beginning *Letters* prior to MacLane's visit, but given the entry's very early appearance in the text the ed. suggests auctorial back-dating.

21. *too tame* - This was common, if not universal, critical and popular opinion.

21. *no distinction* - A quote from Owen Meredith's very popular story-poem *Lucile* - a work Weeks was involved in pirating - *cf.* http://sdrc.lib.uiowa.edu/lucile/publishers/weeks/WEEKS.HTM (accessed 10 May 2015). Orig.: *But the stupid and mischievous boy, that uproots / The exotics, and tramples the tender young shoots, / For a boy's brutal pastime, and only because / He knows no distinction 'twixt heart's-ease and haws, - / One would wish, for the sake of each nursling so nipped / To catch the young rascal and have him well whipped*

24. *with reluctant* - From Longfellow's poem "Maidenhood" (pub. 1842): *Standing, with reluctant feet, / Where the brook and river meet, / Womanhood and childhood fleet!* Cf. *Human Days* (2014) p 556 n 60.

30. *bigoty* - A most offensive phrase, from the slave-owning South: ill-tempered and rebellious.

30. *"fee"* - Presumably a tippable waiter, *i.e.*, one who provides prompt and personal service; in 19th c., to "fee a waiter" was to leave a tip.

31. *anemone ladies* - Reference to MacLane's senior-class literature teacher, Fannie Corbin, on whom she had a famed crush; referred to throughout *Story/I Await*; MacLane's described feelings for Ms. Corbin are a notable early appearance in serious American writing.

31. *Potiphar* - Genesis 39:1-20.

31. *Jack Martin* - An untraceable ref.

35. *were springing* - From Heine's poem "The Homeward Journey" (1823-1824) trans. Leland, Charles Godfrey, in *Pictures of Travel*, Schaefer & Koradi, Philadelphia, 1882, p 16; orig.: *A water-maid rose singing / Before me, fair and pale; / And snow-white breasts were springing / Like fountains, 'neath her veil.*

35. *straight and* - A regularly used phrase, *e.g.*, in title of Nye, Ephraim H.: *The Straight and Narrow Way: Doctrines the Saviour Taught*, Middle States Mission, Cincinnati, 1903.

37. *outmatch the* - At present, an unidentifiable quotation.

38. *lingers* - From Byron's career-boosting Orientalist poem "The Giaour" (pub. 1813). Orig.: *(Before Decay's effacing fingers / Have swept the lines where Beauty lingers)*.

38. *relume* - From *Othello* V:2. Orig.: *I know not where is that Promethean heat / That can thy light relume.*

43. *sink their* - Evidently original.

44-46. *The Glamour* - Evidently original.

47. *inconsistences* - An accepted older spelling.

50. *nor hot* - Revelations 3:15-16: *I know thy works, that thou art neither cold nor hot: I would thou wert cold or hot. So then because thou art lukewarm, and neither cold nor hot, I will spue thee out of my mouth.* (King James)

51. *son of* - From Isaiah 14:12: *How art thou fallen from heaven, O Lucifer, son of the morning! how* art *thou cut down to the ground, which didst weaken the nations* (King James)

53. *and jeer* - From Bulwer-Lytton's 1838 melodrama *The Lady of Lyons; or, Love and Pride*, III:2 (spoken by Pauline): *O fool! O dupe! O wretch! I see it all; / The by-word and the jeer of every tongue / In Lyons! Hast thou in thy heart one touch / Of human kindness?*

54. *love is* - From Romans 13:10: *Love worketh no ill to his neighbour: therefore love is the fulfilling of the law.* (King James)

55. *with you* - Alteration of celebrated phrase by poet Ella Wheeler Wilcox (1850-1919): "Laugh, and the world laughs with you; Weep, and you weep alone" (from "Solitude," 1883).

56. *divers* - Older spelling of "diverse."

57. *best bower* - In certain card-games, extra card added into pack which becomes card of highest value; also, a ship's spare anchor slightly more heavy than that normally used.

58. *angel of* - 2 Corinthians 11:14: *And no marvel; for Satan himself is transformed into an angel of light.* (King James)

60-61. *woman there* - Evidently original.

63. *placed at* - From Genesis 3:24: *So he drove out the man; and he placed at the east of the garden of Eden Cherubims, and a flaming sword which turned every way, to keep the way of the tree of life.* (King James)

64. *more durable* - From Samuel Johnson: *To raise monuments more durable than brass, and more conspicuous than pyramids, has been long the common boast of literature* (*The Rambler*, 23 Mar 1751).

69. *brief authority* - From *Measure for Measure* II:2 (spoken by Isabella): *but man, proud man, / Drest in a little brief authority, / Most ignorant of what he's most assured*

71. *the Spanish* - Poss. ref. to once-popular dramatic poem by George Eliot: *The Spanish Gypsy* (1864-1868).

72. *man is* - From the "Missionary Hymn," words by Reginald Heber (1819); used in Methodist services; orig.: *What though the spicy breezes, / Blow soft o'er Ceylon's isle, / Though every prospect pleases, / And only man is vile.*

76. *Shamrock III* - Britain's sloop, lost against New York Yacht Club's *Reliance* in 1903 America's Cup. *Shamrock IV* would meet similar fate in 1920 Cup race.

76. *Serbian* - Likely that of King Alexander I and his wife, Queen Draga, on 11 June 1903.

77. *Giron* - Ref. to popular Archduchess Louise of Austria (AKA Luise of Austria, 1870-1947); her rebellious behavior at court and subsequent divorce in February 1903 from Crown Prince of Saxony Frederick Augustus (1865-1932) was a sustained scandal in its time; she was rumored, evidently falsely, to have become pregnant by her children's French tutor.

78. *Duchess of* - Consuelo Vanderbilt (1877-1964), whose 1895 society marriage to Charles Spencer-Churchill, 9th Duke of Marlborough (1871-1934), was internationally attended-to; they would separate in 1906.

84. *moat* - Sic.

85. *the fair* - Evidently original.

85. *Mulciber* - Variant name for Vulcan; in Milton's *Paradise Lost* "the architect of the demon city of Pandæmonium"; *cf.* http://en.wikipedia.org/wiki/Mulciber (accessed 10 May 2015).

87. *ether of* - An untraceable quotation.

89. *any way* - An earlier form.

90. *entertained* - Hebrews 13:2: *Be not forgetful to entertain strangers: for thereby some have entertained angels unawares.* (King James)

94. *every where* - An earlier form.

94. *Vamoser* - "Vamose" is an older variant spelling.

101. *loth* - Older spelling of "loath."

103. *but he came* - Likely a deliberate echo of *I Await*, entry of 31 Mar 1902; *cf.* *Human Days* (2014) pp 106, 560 n 106.

*

110. *Revere Beach* - Popular "people's beach" several miles north of Boston's downtown; first public beach in US, featured numerous amusements; poss. ref. to MacLane's 1902 article on visiting Coney Island; *cf. Human Days* (2014) pp 137-142.

111. *goo-goos* - Eyes. The "graceful fairies, with peroxide hair" interestingly preview the Flapper type.

113. *Riverside* - Prob. ref. to area in Auburndale, Massachusetts; Chestnut Hill Reservoir (constr. 1870) is nearby.

114. *little Fido* - Ref. to MacLane's bedside clock mentioned in *Story/I Await*: "Always I take a little clock to bed with me and hang it by a cord at the head of my bed, for company. I have named the clock Little Fido because it is so constant and ticks always. It is beginning to stand in the same relation to me as J.T. Trowbridge's magazine. If I were to go away from here I should take Little Fido and the magazine with me." - *Human Days* (2014) p 94; clock became nationally famed; *cf., e.g.,* "Mary Maclane Discovered - Cambridge Boys Follow Her Through the Street, Quoting Extracts from Her Book - Police Look On," *Boston Daily Globe*, 26 Jul 1902, p 8.

114. *Norumbega Park* - Recreation area with amusement park in Auburndale, Massachusetts (oper. 1897-1963); as with Revere Beach, signals Lizzie's plebeian tastes.

114. *Salem Street* - "...which starts off obliquely from Hanover Street and then runs parallel with it ... It is a curious street, with strange denizens. In early Colony days it was fair Green Lane, upon which it was the dream of prospering Bostonians to live." - Bacon,

Edwin Monroe: *Boston: A Guide Book*, Ginn & Co., Boston, 1903, p 56.

115. John L. Sullivan (1858-1918) - "The Boston Strong Boy"; first gloved boxing Heavyweight Champion, final heavyweight bare-knuckle champion under London Prize Ring Rules; James John "Gentleman Jim" Corbett (1866-1933), American World Heavyweight Champion, defeater of Sullivan in 1892; James Jackson Jeffries (1875-1953), American World Heavyweight Champion and defeater of Corbett (1900 & 1903) and Sharkey (1898 & 1899); Tom "Sailor Tom" Sharkey (1873-1953), champion Irish boxer, defeater of Corbett (1898), loser to Jeffries (1898 & 1899). On MacLane and Sharkey, cf. *Human Days* (2014) pp 293, 295, 328, 573 n 293.

115. *Jimmie Flaherty* - Poss. unrecorded African-American boxer.

116. Richard K. Fox (1846-1922) - Publisher of the *Police Gazette*; "Fox also popularized the presentation of title belts. Prior to the July 8, 1889 fight between Sullivan and Jake Kilrain, another bout he backed, Fox presented Kilrain with a lavish belt made from 200 ounces of solid silver and decorated with diamond-studs and gold ornaments. In the name of the Police Gazette, he issued belts to champions in various weight classes." - http://www.ibhof.com/pages/about/inductees/nonparticipant/fox.html (accessed 10 May 2015)

116. *Chelsea to Roxbury* - Towns flanking Boston in approx. north-south line.

117. *ammonia* - Ref. to MacLane's Anemone Lady.

117. Dan Daly (1858-1904) - American musical comedy performer; ref. is to song "I Annex It" (mus. Ludwig Englander, lyr. J. Cheever Goodwin) in musical comedy *The Cadet Girl*; Daly sang same in role of Baron Chartreuse on Broadway Jul-Sep 1900, subsequently in Boston area (*cf.* advert., *Harvard Lampoon*, 19 Oct 1900, p 23).

118. *quote Kip* - ref. to Rudyard Kiping's patriotic poem "The Absent-Minded Beggar" (1899) (mus. Sir Arthur Sullivan) - has line "pass the hat for your credit's sake, and pay - pay - pay!"

119. *one, two, three as horrible as it is* - Per orig.

120. *seven-masters* - Poss. shoes made by an apprentice who worked so shoddily he'd been passed off by six cobblers to a final.

122. Mane Waddy - Not any known person; poss. parody of Mary Baker Eddy.

123. *frontispiece* - Viewable at https://books.google.com/books?id=4_wTAAAAYAAJ& printsec=frontcover#v=onepage&q&f=false (accessed 10 May 2015).

123. *a la Maryland* - In many versions (partic. Escoffier's), served with some sort of banana garnish; thus, out of season in winter.

123. *biograph* - Motion picture. Ref. to The Biograph Co., AKA American Mutoscope & Biograph Co. (1895-1928); *cf. Human Days* (2014) p 591 n 476.

123. *Nick Carter* - Fictional private detective; first appeared 1886; on MacLane's mention of Nick Carter, *cf. Human Days* (2014) pp 402, 585 n 402.

123. *rubber* - Look with turned head in the manner of a rubber-necking tourist. *cf.* p 164 of present vol. for "rubbers".

123. *Elevated* - Boston Elevated Railway (late 1890s-1947).

123. *sen-sen* - Breath freshener (orig. "breath perfume"), inaug. late 19th c. by T.B. Dunn Co.; major aroma would be liquorice.

123. *women who know* - *Cf.* McKown, pp 72-81 herein; MacLane also takes them on in "A Foreground and a Background," *Denver Post*, 4 Oct 1903; in *Human Days* (2014) p 245-248.

124. *three hundred and twenty ... $1.10 net* - Story was c. 320 pages long and priced at $1.50.

*

129. *January 13, 1902* - Story/*I Await* begins on 13 Jan 1901.

130. Russell Sage (1816-1906) - Prominent partner of the dubious Jay Gould in various financing deals; President and Vice-President of the Chicago, Milwaukee & St. Paul Railway for twelve years.

130. *for temperance* - Butte was known as one of the most wildly alcoholphile places in the US.

130. Warm Springs - Town in western Georgia; famed then, as now, for warm mineral springs.

130. *Town Topics* - *Cf. Human Days* (2014) pp 257, 569 n 257.

131. *out the gas* - Commit suicide by extinguishing illuminating flame and allowing natural gas to fill a room.

135. *Omar* - Ref. to preface (1889) by Justin Huntly McCarthy, quoted by MacLane in

Story/I Await: Alas *for Me, alas for all who weep / And wonder at the Silence dark and deep / That girdles round this little Lamp in space / No wiser than when Omar fell asleep*; cf. *Human Days* (2014) pp 33, 302, 554 n 33.

140. *inquisition* - Non-capitalized per orig.

140. *foolish factory* - Pop. expression of time for lunatic asylum, more generally "crazy place" or expressive of exasperation: "ready for the foolish factory." Shores' is earliest use ed. has found in book sources; earliest newspaper source found is sports item: "Reading in the medical department of a well known daily that chewing gum held many persons from the foolish factory and prevented the already batty ones from becoming violent, Mr. Tebeau thought he had the trouble located. He purchased a job lot of the stuff and fed it into the maps of Willie Schriver and his pals. The result was something wonderful." - *Saint Paul Globe* [Minnesota], 21 Aug 1903, p 5; term started to appear in newspapers in late 1903, books after *c.* 1904; it lasted through the 1910s.

141. *of Don* - Early in *Story/I Await*, MacLane writes "It is the Byron of *Don Juan* in whom I find suggestions of myself" - *Human Days* (2014) p 17; cf. pp 18, 87, 553 n 17, 558 n 87.

141. *silent sarcophagus* - An untraceable quotation, poss. original.

142. Sapolio - Well-advertised brand of soap, introduced 1869.

143. *Central* - Telephone exchange, then staffed by live operators.

145. *union suits* - Variety of long, one-piece underwear.

145. *padded hips* - In *Story/I Await*, MacLane writes "...by an ingenious arrangement of my striped moreen petticoat I contrive to display a more evident pair of hips than Nature seems to have intended for me at this stage." - *Human Days* (2014) p 95.

145. *singing stomachs* - Ref. to *Story/I Await*: "My calm beautiful stomach silently sings as I walk a song of peace, the while it hugs within itself the chyme that was my lunch." - *Human Days* (2014) p 26.

145. *fol-lol* - "'Fol lol the doh fol the day, Fol the doh fol the day,' is ancient Irish mouth-music which is common in traditional music." - http://en.wikipedia.org/wiki/Theme_from_Harry%27s_Game (accessed 10 May 2015).

145. *cambric* - Ref. to *Story/I Await*: "In the front of my shirt-waist there are nine cambric handkerchiefs cunningly distributed." - *Human Days* (2014) p 95.

145. *gently resting livers* - Ref. to *Story/I Await*: "My sound sensitive liver rests gently with

its thin yellow bile in sweet content." - *Human Days* (2014) p 26.

145. *on cigar* - Poss. ref. to MacLane's visage on cigar boxes; *cf.*, *e.g.*, "And Now It Is The Mary M'lane [*sic*.] Cigar - Butte's literary genius lends her signature to a tobacco manufacturer - Lillian Russell et al must now go way back - you may have a pure Havana filler from a box adorned with highly embellished labels picturing the youthful writer - will soon be on the market - C.M. Neilsen secures right to use the trade mark." - *Butte Inter Mountain* [Montana], 18 Jun 1902, p 1

147. *so intensely heroic* - Ref. to *Story/I Await*: "There was Charlotte Corday - a heroine whom I admire above all the heroines ... What must be the exalted ecstasy of Charlotte Corday's soul now! - *Human Days* (2014) p 82; *cf.* pp 496, 520, 558 n 82.

147. *pig-pen to do with anything.* - No terminal question mark per orig.

148. *[every]* - Ed.'s insertion; orig.: "... the thing that is mingled with word."

148. *a neurotic* - Sic.; in original ed. of *Story/I Await*, publisher rendered ms. "narcotic" as "neurotic."

149. *play even* - *I.e.*, if Willie makes as much as MacLane, he'll have no need of risky games of chance, *i.e.*, be rich enough to play at 50-50 odds.

*

153. *walkin' delegate* - Representative of labor union; charged with visiting various worksites and talking to workers to check conditions.

154. Robert G. Ingersoll (1833-1899) - Prominent American agnostic orator, known as "The Great Agnostic"; friend of Whitman, sensationally popular particularly for his unstoppably eloquent attacks on Christianity.

154. Anna Held (1872-1918) - Celebrated sparkling French actress, singer, lyricist, composer; appeared in US starting 1896; appeared in several silent films but most famed for onstage beauty and flirtatiousness.

154. *banjo eye* - Pop. phrase ref. to large-eyed, attentive look (apparently variously enamored, shocked, stunned, more rarely poss. dubious or skeptical); appears to be term's earliest appearance in book form; later appearance (only other found by ed.) in Ade, George: *The Girl Proposition: A Bunch of He and She Fables*, Harper & Bros, New York, [*c.* Nov.] 1902, p 101: "For some Reason, the latest variety of New Woman resents the Suggestion that she is a Soft Mark for the curbstone Masher who stands in front of Cigar Stores and Works the Banjo Eye"; for quote from book mentioning MacLane, *cf.* p 168

herein; earliest newspaper appear. found by ed. is *Hawaiian Gazette* (Honolulu, Oahu), 5 Apr 1901, p 5: "All of the ladies and gentlemen were highly excited, all of them except the loving couple who were united in th bonds of matrimony by the captain of the Peking the day before the vessel's arrival here. Those were off in a corner by themselves, making banjo eyes and telling each other that they were sweeter than all the sugar cane in the Hawaiian Islands." Deposit copies of popular song "The Girl with the Banjo Eye" (mus. & lyr. Karl Weixelbaum) were received by Library of Congress on 3 Oct 1902 per *Catalogue of Title Entries of Books and Other Articles Entered in the Office of the Register of Copyrights, Library of Congress, at Washington, D.C. - Vol. 33:* Library of Congress, Copyright Office, Washington, D.C., 1902, p 431.

154. *Gaston an' Alphonse* - Ref. to comic strip by Frederick Burr Opper of two clumsy yet overly-polite Frenchmen; ran in Hearst papers, syndicated through at least late 1903.

155. *Centerville ghost* - Ref. to MacLane's supposed identification as "the Centerville ghost": a spectral character given to wandering certain areas of Butte late at night clad in black; identification never confirmed; earliest known appear. of claim is lengthy article in *Butte Inter Mountain* [Montana], 3 May 1902, p 14: "Mystery No Longer Shrouds Famous Centerville Ghost - Wandering in the gloaming and the dawning in her search for the devil Miss MacLane appeared as an apparition to the people of the suburb."

157. Dud Rickard (?-1903) - Once-famed Montana cowboy. "Within a month we have heard of the death of 'Dud Rickard,' who in the '60s hauled freight over the Benton-Helena trail, and who could handle a bull-whip with the best of them. After thirty-eight years of freighting in Montana, he died in the poorhouse, a physical wreck, deserted even by his own family. He was in many ways typical of this fearless class of fellows who blazed the trails into nature's wilds and made it possible for civilization to advance; a class quite as distinctive as that of the far-famed 'cowboys,' and passing away even more rapidly." - Matteson, Sumner W., "The Passing of the Bull-Whacker," *Atlantic Monthly*, Nov 1903, p 272.

159. *Heins affirmed* - Misspelling: German poet Heinrich Heine (1797-1856); ref. to his poem "Ich rief den Teufel, und er kam", trans. by Emma Lazarus (1881) as "I Called the Devil and He Came" - first lines: *I called the devil and he came, / His face with wonder I must scan; / He is not ugly, he is not lame, / He is a delightful, charming man. / A man in the prime of life, in fact, / Courteous, engaging and full of tact. / A diplomat, too, of wide research / Who cleverly talks about state and church.*

164. *a Golden* - Ref. to 1896 novel by Richard Le Gallienne (1866-1947), *Quest of the Golden Girl; cf.* pretend correspondence between MacLane and Le Gallienne pp 163-165 herein; MacLane and Le Gallienne were occasionally mentioned together in the media,

166. *Casey's* - Apparently disreputable Atlanta saloon; almost undocumented; rare excep-

tion in *Life*, 28 Mar 1895, p 198: "The Atlanta detectives have at last done a public service. They have 'sized up' Eugene Field and A. Conan Doyle. They looked at the photographs of those persons, handed to them by an inquisitive reporter, and said they recognized them as well-known and unmistakable 'crooks.' ... As for Eugene Field, there are few Americans who read at all who do not know, with almost legal knowledge, that he was guilty of betraying the secrets of Casey's infamous *table d'hote* ..."

171. *glory gentleman* - A pastiche of Miss Morning Glory in Yone Noguchi's *American Diary of a Japanese Girl* (period. pub. 1901, book pub. 1902) and MacLane's Anemone Lady; for letters from MacLane to Noguchi, *cf. Human Days* (2014) pp 274-275, 570 n 274.

172. John MacGinnis (1867-1936) - Vice-Pres. of United Copper Company in Butte; close associate of the Jovian F. Augustus Heinze, on whom *cf. Human Days* (2014) pp 517, 594 n 517.

174. Jack Munroe (1877-1942) - Heavyweight boxer born in Nova Scotia; known as "The Cape Breton Miner"; resident of Butte in his youth - was classmate of MacLane's; his and her early fame started around the same time; last fight in 1906.

174. Senator Clark - *Cf. Human Days* (2014) pp 147, 517, 519, 563 n 147, 576 n 318.

175. *Boston* - In 1908, MacLane had moved from Boston to Manhattan.

176. *bombard* - Obs. term for sizable leathern liquor container in form of bottle or jug.

176. *ever a rocky road* - Not, evidently, a quotation.

176. *abiding place ... crank* - Curious crib of line from William Cowper Brann ("Brann the Iconoclast") (1855-1898), American journalist noted for sharply forceful articulateness; published newspaper *The Iconoclast*; orig. in "The Kansas Trinity," reprin. *The Complete Works of Brann the Iconoclast*, Brann Publishers, New York, 1919, Vol. 5, p 240: "Fair, if somewhat faded flowers of Kansas, the abiding place of the blooming bigot and home of the crinose [*i.e.*, hairy] crank, indeed you do me wrong."

176 *Newbro's* - Large, popular drug store in Butte, creator in 1902 of the "Mary MacLane High-Ball" drink ("With or without ice cream - cooling, refreshing, invigorating, devilish - the up-to-date drink at our soda fountain") - *cf.* advert., *Butte Inter Mountain* [Montana], 16 May 1902, p 4.

176. *Hudibrastic* - Mock-heroic iambic-tetrametric form constructed by Samuel Butler for his poem *Hudibras* (1663-1678).

176. *Lavelle's rigs* - An untraceable ref.

176. *trilbies* - Feet.

176, *dote, yet* - Spoken by Iago in *Othello*, Act III, sc. 3: *Who dotes, yet doubts, suspects, yet strongly loves!*

176-177. *a [hen] feather pillow* - Ed.'s speculative reading.

177. *he-Anenome, [of?] ... off the [k?]nee* - Ed.'s speculative readings.

177. *airy nymph* - Quote of *Ode XLII* by Thomas Moore (1779-1852): *Some airy nymph, with fluent limbs, / Through the dance luxuriant swims, / Waving, in her snowy hand, / The leafy Bacchanalian wand, / Which, as the tripping wanton flies, / Shakes its tresses to her sighs!* On Moore, *cf. Human Days* (2014) pp 553 n 27, 557 n 72, 566 n 198, 574 n 298.

178. *the past* - From title of poem "Nay, let the Past be past, nor strive in vain" (1883) by Frances Anne (Fanny) Kemble (1809-1893).

178. *Troilus stood* - Evidently a humorously-meant original.

178. Thomas William Lawson (1857-1925) - *cf. Human Days* (2014) p 571 n 282.

178. *Buckets* - An untraceable ref.

178. *Two Bit Billie* - William Parsons (?-1903), a once-familiar figure in Butte; property man at city's Grand Opera, became cocaine and morphine addict, died indigent; *cf. Butte Inter Mountain* (Montana), 3 Sep 1903, p 2; *cf.* also *ibid.*, 31 Aug 1903, p 5

178. *Mickey the Greek* - Patrick McAtesney (?-early 1901), a well-known Butte vagrant; "'Mickey,' the good-natured vagabond, is well-known and well-liked, particularly by those who had the pleasure of seeing him dance for his supper. But among all his many friends and acquaintances there were none who knew him by any other name than 'Mickey, the Greek,' a name that was possibly conferred upon him because of his powerful, perfectly modeled torso and his finely chiseled head. Mickey is a pretty good 'chisler' himself, particularly so at the end of a jail sentence, but that had nothing to do with his nickname, of course. (Nov., 1899)" - "Echoes from the Distant Past," *Montana Standard* [Butte], 21 Dec 1941, p 35.

179. *Gladys* - An untraceable ref.

179. *Callihan the Bum* - John Callahan (1868-1898), a much reported-on Butte vagrant, drunkard, occasional petty larcenist; first known mention in *Anaconda Standard* [Montana], 14 Aug 1891, p 8; reports of occasional sobriety reforms start in 1895; convictions for vagrancy continue after; death reported in *Anaconda Standard*, 28 Mar 1898, p 6.

179. Stanley Ketchel - *Cf. Human Days* (2014) pp 496, 592 n 496.

179. *wife ... A.B.C.* - An untraceable ref.; poss. to imagined scenario of marrying random person chosen from, *e.g.*, the telephone directory.

179. *Nine Mile House ... to Homestake* - Driving from then-popular bar, located nine miles southeast of Butte, up to mining district on East Ridge of Continental Divide, *i.e.*, up a significant grade - an extreme difficulty for automobiles of the time.

180. *largest chimney* - Ref. to "The Big Stack" at B&M smelter in Great Falls, Montana; built by Boston & Montana Consol. Copper & Silver Mining Co. (predecessor to the mighty Anaconda Copper) - at 508 ft., tallest chimney in the world in period 1908-1914; demolished 1982.

180. Joseph Moore Dixon (1867-1934) - Republican politician from Montana; state's seventh Governor; Progressive; campaign manager for Theodore Roosevelt in 1912, chaired Convention that nominated Roosevelt on the "Bull Moose" ticket for President.

181. Charles S. Warren (1846-1921) - Began as bull-driver, then sequentially was school teacher (while placer mining in summer), sheriff, Butte's first police magistrate, clerk of U.S. District Court, member of state Constitutional Convention, Presidential elector for state; established mining company, realty company, and in Butte co-founded the Intermountain Publishing Company.

181. *Monroe* - Misspelling of "Jack Munroe"; *cf.* present vol. p 216 n 174.

181. *Dick Kilroy* - Richard R. Kilroy (1871-poss. 1942), Irish-born Montana educator, journalist, associate of mining magnates; by 1902 was former principal of *Butte High School* and held position on editorial staff of *Butte Inter Mountain* (*cf. Butte Inter Mountain* [Montana], 14 Apr 1902, p 9); in 1909 was, under tumultuous circumstances, elected director of Heinze's United Copper Co. (*Daily Missoulian* [Montana], 3 Jun 1909, p 1); by 1912 was former manager of *Butte Evening News* and had become manager of *Missoula Sentinel* (*Daily Missoulian* [Montana], 7 Apr 1912, p 10); two years later was associated with Heinze's former foe, Amalgamated Copper Mining Co. (which would shortly become Anaconda) in opposing worker's compensation measure (*Daily Missoulian*, 12 Sep 1914, p 1); in 1922 was named to advisory committee for Montana State University's school of journalism at Missoula (*Great Falls Tribune* [Montana], 10 Sep 1922, p 12).

183. Heinie Zimmerman (1887-1969) - Major League infielder for Chicago Cubs and New York Giants (1907-1919); the point of the joke is at present obscure.

184. *in Cuba* - Humorous ref. to former Pres. Theodore Roosevelt's repute as individualistic adventurer; no such title or anything similar is among his works.

185. Ralph Graves (1900-1977) - American actor, sometime director and screenwriter; appeared as the Callow Youth in MacLane's 1918 silent film *Men Who Have Made Love to Me*; afterward was associate of Howard Hughes and Frank Capra; on film, cf. *Human Days* (2014) p 536.

185. *to oblige* - An unclear ref.

185. *gay deceiver* - Expression of the time for a seducer.

190. *Mount Pelee* - Ref. to catastrophic 1902 eruption of Mount Pelée in the Lesser Antilles; killed c. 30,000 people; MacLane was often compared to it in terms of power and temperament.

190. Maria Hicks [?-?, *fl.* 1900-1902] - Eccentric female vagrant/vandal in mid-West US; first known newspaper mention: "Maria is known to every police officer along the Northern Pacific road in North Dakota, where she has been a constant traveler for years. She drops in on a town, breaks a few windows, for which she has a mania, and the police promptly buy her a ticket and send her on to the next town. In this way she travels constantly, gets her name in the papers and seems to enjoy life. It is claimed Maria belongs in Brown county, South Dakota ..." - *Bismarck Weekly Tribune* [North Dakota], 3 Mar 1900, p 8; final known mention in *Dakota Farmers' Leader* [Canton, South Dakota], 3 Jul 1903, p 2.

190. *Cherry sisters* - Cf. *Human Days* (2014) pp 333, 579 n 333.

191. Louis A. Disbrow (186?-?) - New York man charged with double murder of romantic interest Sarah Lawrence and rival for her affections; acquitted in 1903; became famed in automobile racing circles.

192. *Mt Clemens* - Then known as "Bath City of America" for mineral baths; prob. ref. to temperature of waters.

194. *eastern preacher* - An untraceable ref.

194. Samuel Eberly Gross (1843-1913) - Prominent Illinois real-estate developer; wrote comedy play *The Merchant Prince of Corneville*, perf. England Nov. 1896; believed Edmond Rostand plagiarized in *Cyrano de Bergerac* (1897); successfully sued in Chicago court, which fined Rostand $1 in damages (given by Gross to charity); *Cyrano* was enjoined from performance for a time; in 1910 Gross accused Rostand ("a literary thief") of additional plagiarism from *Prince* in *Chantecler* and cabled French Academy demanding investigation (*San Francisco Call*, 22 Feb 1910, p 4); no record of any French concern; point of ref. seems to be painting MacLane and Gross as tough, prickly, but marginal figures.

196. *arrest* - Ref. to MacLane's having been arrested in Rockland, Mass. in Oct 1902 for mistakenly trespassing at the home of author Maria Louise Pool (*Daily Northwestern* [Evanston, Illinois], 21 Oct 1902, p 5).

196. Elsie Viola Larsen (1886-1962) - Perhaps the most notable MacLane fan; Chicago-based; was in newspapers from 1902 (for stealing a doctor's horse-and-carriage to get color for a planned book) to the later 1940s (as animal welfare crusader known in 1930s to carry hatchet and shotgun for threat and/or use).

198. *went back* - MacLane moved back to Butte from New York in Dec 1909 and was soon stricken by scarlet fever with diphtheritic complications; for a time her life was despaired-of; illness, and recovery some weeks later, made national news.

198. *fat man* - Ref. to her syndicated article "Mary MacLane Wants a Vote - For the Other Woman"; *cf. Human Days* (2014) pp 318-323.

198. *pickles in their shirt* - Poss. ref to 1902 interview during which MacLane dropped olives into her shirt-waist; *cf. Human Days* (2014) p 129.

199. Elliot Dexter (1870-1941) - American vaudevillian and, from 1916 on, movie actor; retired 1925; his confessional article (poss. influenced by MacLane's film *Men Who Have Made Love to Me*, based on her 1910 *Butte Evening News* feature article) pub. *Photoplay*, May 1918, pp 18-21, 107; for MacLane's article, *cf. Human Days* (2014) p 324-331.

*

THIS
BOOK HAS
BEEN SET IN
ADOBE GARAMOND
PRO, A FONT BY ROBT.
SLIMBACH SPECIFICALLY
FOR DIGITAL TYPESETTING.
PERSONAL INSPECTION OF C.
GARAMOND'S ORIGINAL PUNCHES
INSPIRED A DESIGN FAITHFUL TO THE
ORIGINAL ROMAN TYPE, WHICH
TRADITIONALLY HAS BEEN
PAIRED WITH THE MORE
SLOPED, ENERGETIC
ITALICS CUT BY
R. GRANJON.

*

BOOK
DESIGN
HAS, IN YEARS
RECENT, DEPARTED
FROM CLASSICAL STRICTURES
AGAINST TYPOGRAPHICAL WIDOWS
AND ORPHANS. GIVEN THE NATURE
OF THIS TEXT, THE DECISION WAS
MADE TO HOLD RIGIDLY TO
PAGEBLOCK GEOMETRY
AND PERMIT WIDOWS
AND ORPHANS
FREELY.

*

* COMING NEXT *

Mary MacLane - a 19-year-old diarist from the early 20th century, still influential today - was the first of the modern media personalities. Now, her whole story is being told in a series of books from Petrarca Press.

On the heels of the successful launch of a 600-page anthology, *Human Days: A Mary MacLane Reader*, we are proud to announce forthcoming release of two new books in our MacLane Series: *Mary in The Press: Miss MacLane & Her Fame* and the first-ever complete study of MacLane's life, career, and influence, *A Quite Unusual Intensity of Life: The Lives, Works, and Influence of Mary MacLane*.

Mary in The Press provides, for the first time, more than one thousand pages of interviews, news stories, reminiscences, attacks, opinions, plaudits, personal letters, cartoons, photographs, and more - almost all unseen for a century. With a detailed introduction and lengthy footnotes and bibliography, this mammoth two-volume edition unfolds for the first time the enormous controversy - and adoration - over the writer a forthcoming PBS documentary calls "The First Woman of the Twentieth Century."

A Quite Unusual Intensity of Life goes beyond the usual biography to unfold Mary MacLane's inner and outer worlds; the people she knew and loved; her influences, and her influence on the future; her life outside of writing as a gambler extraordinaire and silent film writer/star; the inner secrets of her unique, still-compelling literary style - and much more.

Michael R. Brown, foremost MacLane scholar in the world today, says of these two books: "This is the other half of Mary's story, and it's taken decades of research to tell it. She gave herself totally in her writing, and the world's slowly remembering now. These are the books I wish I'd had at my side when I read those first words, thirty years ago."

Check http://marymaclane.com for exclusive content, updates, and all news about the ongoing discovery of Mary MacLane. For publication information and pre-ordering for *Mary in The Press* and *A Quite Unusual Intensity of Life*, email groupmail@petrarcapress.com or dial 530-566-6615. ISBN and SAN information forthcoming.

*

Adobe Garamond Pro * Body: 11.5 pts, lead: 12 pts. * Notes: 10 pts, lead: 11 pts. *
Page: 6in. x 9in. * Margins: top 1 in., bottom 1.375 in., inner 0.91 in., outer 0.7213 in.
Text width 4.3687 in. * Normal indent: 0.1667 in. * Fleuron from LTC Vine Leaves

Made in the USA
Lexington, KY
02 April 2016